# Clay Lowder, MD

# WINNERS TRAVEL

## A Doctor's Guide to Mental, Physical, and Spiritual Health

# Clay Lowder, MD

Printed in the United States of America

First Printing, 2019

Published by Redwood Publishing, LLC (Ladera Ranch, California)
www.redwooddigitalpublishing.com

Disclaimer: Although the author and publisher have made every effort to ensure that the information in this book was correct at press time, the author and publisher do not assume and hereby disclaim any liability to any party for any loss, damage, or disruption caused by errors or omissions, whether such errors or omissions result from negligence, accident, or any other cause. Separately, this book is designed to provide information and motivation to its readers. It is sold with the understanding that the author and publisher are not engaged to render any type of psychological, legal, or any other kind of professional advice. The content of each article is the sole expression and opinion of its author and is not meant to substitute for any advice from your healthcare professionals, lawyers, therapists, business advisors/partners, or personal connections.

ISBN 978-1-947341-67-8 (hardcover)
ISBN 978-1-947341-75-3 (paperback)
ISBN 978-1-947341-79-1 (e-book)

Library of Congress Cataloging Number: 2019910204

Cover Design: Michelle Manley
Interior Design: Ghislain Viau

10 9 8 7 6 5 4 3 2 1

# Dedication

Winners Travel didn't just happen. This is my life's work. I totally couldn't have done it without a ton of support and love. Thank you to all of you!

Thank you Lord that everything happens for a reason.

I hereby dedicate this book to my family. Without the Lowder there is no Lowderisms. Without the Ariail there is no writing. Thank you Mama and Daddy!

To my dear children—you are my true joy. You are also my life's work.

Clayton, you have my passion and enthusiasm. You have that gleam in your eye.

Coker, you are my counselor. You are my miracle and the glue of our family.

Liza Lu, yes, you are the perfect one. You will carry the writing torch. You know what I love about you?...yes, everything!

To my high school sweetheart, KD, what a love story. You are still the one who makes me smile, still the one who makes me laugh, and I couldn't have done it without you. Thank you for letting me run everywhere I go.

Winners Travel!

Clay

# Table of Contents

# Foreword
## By Liza Lowder

"SHHH. BE QUIET, LIZA! I can hear him coming," my mom whispered to me as we were crouched down together in a cabinet, hiding from my dad.

"Where are y'all? I'm going to have to do it eventually, so you might as well just come out," yelled my dad from just around the corner of our hiding spot.

It was flu season, which meant flu shots for the Lowder family, a not-so-welcomed ritual by all but my dad, who found it amusing to torment us with those shots. Around the same time every year, he would bring home five flu shots and would usually deliver the news to us during a nice family dinner. Each year, this was my mom's and my cue to haul butt and run for the hills, which would eventually lead to an adult game of hide-and-seek. If you're wondering, we have never missed a flu shot (turns out, our hiding tactics were never quite enough).

Having grown up as a doctor's daughter, the pull for me to go into medicine has been rather strong all of my life, whether from my dad himself, other family members, or even random people I've met. However, I have made it quite clear since the time I could talk that teaching is my passion. Despite all of the negative feedback I have received over the years when declaring this passion to others, one might say I have stayed strong, considering I'm now majoring in secondary education and English at Clemson University now. It has only been within the past year or so that I decided more specifically that I wanted to teach high school English, due to my love for writing.

Why do I tell you this? Because even though such a large part of my dad's life has been dedicated to medicine, I believe that my passion for teaching, and even English in a way, came from him. "Doctor" comes from the Latin word "teacher," ya know.

My dad loves words. I say that in such general terms because I don't mean that he is necessarily an eloquent speaker all of the time, because, in fact, his redneck tendencies often emerge when he is speaking (and even writing.) I say that my dad loves words because he *loves* to tell a story; he loves to take the knowledge he has attained, whether intellectual, spiritual, or humorous, and share it with others. The most important rule regarding words that my dad has ever taught me is to always start with a story and end with a story, hence the beginning—and, spoiler alert, ending— of this foreword.

Whether it is a piece of writing, a speech, or even just talking to people, he always told me that a story not only keeps the attention of your audience, but lets them see the real you, not just someone who rehearses words to sound great. I would like to say that my dad came up with this tactic of storytelling himself, but he really derived this straight from Jesus Christ himself, as he reveals in the first few pages of his book, "I wrote this book to tell you these stories. Jesus told stories. He used parables and let us draw our own conclusions. I hope you will read mine and reflect. I want you to change." (Lowder, 5). What a better role model to follow than Jesus?

Through his stories, my dad has been able to effectively share the concept of Winners Travel with everybody he meets. Winners Travel has become a famous slogan among everyone who knows my dad, because it truly is embedded into his everyday life. He is the definition of Winners Travel. Y'all, he really does practice what he preaches. In this book you will find all of his sayings, which he and my mom have coined "Lowderisms," beliefs, and the habits he has formed that have helped him achieve his healthiest life, mentally, spiritually, and physically. And, from living with him, I can confirm that he *really* does say and do these things almost every single day.

Winners Travel doesn't just mean planning luxurious trips all the time until you're broke. How you perceive and execute Winners Travel is really up to you, but the baseline is all the same—it's a lifestyle of planning, anticipating, and being proactive so that your life is filled with excitement and improvement. I have to be honest though, and say that I was selfishly a little jealous at first when he told me about this idea for the book, because I didn't want the whole world to know our special family motto. But after seeing the effect it has on people, I am more than thrilled now to share our secret to life with you. In fact, I now think it is imperative that you learn it!

So why should you read this book? It's simple: my dad's *Winners Travel* is a package deal—much like himself. This book will help you become a winner by showing you how to travel to physical, mental, and spiritual health. This book is different from other self-help books because instead of barking instructions at you, it will teach you to live better through the intense, funny, or tear-jerking stories he has used in this book, because they are *real* and relatable. In fact, my friends and I cannot wait for his book to come out. They bug me weekly about when it will finally arrive!

But, why am I worthy enough to write this foreword? Anyone could write a foreword accrediting my dad saying how great he is and how great the book is, but I believe my experience as his daughter, and as most say his "exact replica in girl form," has given me the ability to tell you why you should read this book. As you'll find out in the book, he has been my softball coach since I started playing little leagues at the age of five all the way up until my senior year of high school. We won the state championship that year, by the way.

Everyone that knows him knows that if he could put on our uniform, grab a bat, and join us, he would, but I'm not so sure of how our little softball pants would look on him. He chose to do the next best thing, though, which was to coach us. It is important to know that my dad only does things with 110% effort and enthusiasm … imagine him coaching! All of my teammates can tell you that there was truly "never a dull moment" with him on that softball field. He set up the equipment and cleaned it up afterwards, brought us cookies and brownies, and never failed to deliver a motivational speech or two. Although winning the state championship our senior year was truly unbeatable, there is a different story I want to share with you before I let you dive into his words.

My dad and I definitely butted heads a time or two, (remember when I said that we're basically the same person?) but one time stands out among the rest. It was junior year and to be frank, I was sick of my dad barking at me at practice. I have to be fair and say that I am extra sensitive. But hey, he was extra tough on me compared to my other teammates. He kept yelling, I kept talking back. It was affecting our relationship outside of the softball field, and we both knew it.

One day my dad sat me down at the kitchen table with tears in his eyes and said, "Liza Lu, I love you and you know I'm only tough on you because I want the best for you. But I don't like one bit how this is affecting our relationship, and as much as I love softball and being out there with you, I will stop coming to practice and stop being your coach if it's too much. I just want you to enjoy your last two years of softball and I would be sick if I was the reason it wasn't great."

I proceeded to tell him that softball wouldn't be the same if he stopped coaching, and that it was just something we needed to work on. I tell you this to show you a different side of my dad's character. Most see him as some full-of-life doctor, which he is, but he is so much more. His selflessness is so substantial that he was willing to give up coaching, one of his favorite things, if it meant that I would be happier. Winners are selfless.

So, I want to thank you, Daddy, for writing this for us. Thank you for sharing your ideas and stories that will help us live our lives to the fullest. Thank you for Winners Travel and all it has meant to me since the day you first decided it would be our motto. Thank you for persistently instilling this in not just me and our family, but in everyone you meet. Thank you for persisting enough to write and finish this book amid your busy life. I cannot wait to see how it changes the world! But most importantly, thank you for being the best role model, the best friend, and the best dad to me. You are truly something special!

Hopefully now you have a pretty decent idea now of who I am, who my dad is, and why you are about to read this really cool book. I hope you're ready to start this journey, because as my dad always tells me: be careful … it *will* change your life!

CHAPTER 1

# Everything Happens for a Reason

*"Never a dull moment, never a wasted second!"*
— Coach Faulkner, Seventh-Grade History Class

H E WAS NOT BREATHING. HE was soaking wet. I rolled him over; he was blue.

\* \* \*

It was the summer of 2015, and my family and I were on vacation. We had rented a place at DeBordieu Beach, a secluded, coastal spot near Georgetown, South Carolina, that offers such activities as tennis, golf, and fishing. Although it's thirty minutes from Myrtle Beach, Debordieu is not developed commercially. It's an old-school Carolina beach with sprawling live oaks and we love how removed from the world we feel. As a family, we love to fish, and deeply enjoy the quiet backwater DeBordieu provides.

Earlier that day, my son Coker got out of his car and said, "Dad, something isn't right."

I got in his car, drove it around the block, and boy, was that an understatement. His brakes were gone.

Kelliegh, my wife, followed me into Georgetown to an auto repair shop.

On the way back to the beach house, she said, "Oh, I need to go to the grocery store. Let's go now while we're in town."

I shook my head in stark refusal.

"Coker and I are playing golf," I explained.

After a minute or so of heated discussion, she gave in.

"Typical," she sighed, and shook her head. "I guess I'll go alone."

Lowder men are stubborn. (We also don't like the grocery store.)

Kelliegh reluctantly drove me through the guard gate and then the five miles it took to get back to the house while carefully obeying the strict 25 mph speed limit. On her way back out, she stopped at the guard gate. DeBordieu charges a fee to have a boat at one's vacation rental, and we had both paid the boat fee by accident the day we checked in, so Kelliegh decided she might as well ask for a refund while she was headed back out.

She had just walked up to the window at the gate when she heard the speaker from the radio scanner come to life: "Call all! We've got a drowning! Get 911 here quick! It's a kid!" It was loud and clear.

The male guard froze and looked directly at my wife, clearly hoping she hadn't heard the alarming words.

The female guard tried to dismiss the shocking announcement by asking, "What can I help you with, ma'am?"

The details of the emergency continued to emanate from that small box on the desk of the security booth as Kelliegh attempted to explain that we needed a refund for the boat fee, but she could not seem to get the words out. She and the two guards were distracted by the chilling words they continued to hear from the dispatcher.

"My husband is a doctor!" my wife blurted out. "He is in DeBordieu right now. Where is the kid? What's the address?"

The other guard turned to Kelliegh and dismissively said, "Look, let's just let the EMS handle it."

The three of them stood there awkwardly.

The scanner went off again: "Get them here quick! It looks bad. He was in the pool for a long time! He's blue!"

My wife couldn't stand it any longer.

"Tell me the address, please! My husband is a family doctor. He'll go! He can get there fast, and he can help!"

The female guard, who had been standing on the other side of the booth, heard my wife's plea. She shouted to the male guard, "Oh just tell her!" After the male guard continued to stay silent, she yelled to Kelliegh, "It's 1411 Beach Boulevard! Tell your husband to go . . . now!"

Immediately, my wife called me. I was sitting in my truck in the driveway of our rental house, waiting on Coker, with the truck cranked and ready to go. I answered her call on the first ring, something my family would tell you is rare.

"Clay!" she exclaimed, her voice cracking. "There's a kid drowning! It's 1411 Beach Boulevard. Go now!" she screamed.

I didn't need to hear anything more. I frantically punched the address into my Garmin GPS and hit the gas. Less than a minute later, as I turned down Beach Boulevard, I could see that a crowd had gathered outside one of the beach homes in the neighborhood. There was a young volunteer firefighter kneeling beside a child. I could see that the child was limp.

I slammed the truck into park and sprinted through the crowd.

When I reached the child, I rolled him over onto his back. (The firefighter should have done this, but I think he was in a state of panic or shock.) There were no signs of life. His cheeks were turning a dark purple. I knew what to do, but I was sick inside: this was bad.

I glanced around and saw a big man pacing about ten yards away. He was wearing a red bathing suit with two white stripes down the sides and no shirt. He was soaking wet too, and fervently sobbing. I suspected the home was having a pool party (some of the larger homes in this area had big pools out back), and something had gone wrong.

My training took over, and I began to perform CPR on the child. He had no pulse. I started chest compressions and leaned over to give him mouth-to-mouth resuscitation. Then I saw something: it was a frothy drool.

"What is that?!" I yelled. "Something is in there!"

I tried to pry his mouth open, but his jaw was clenched. I had just completed PALS (Pediatric Advanced Life Support) training, and recalled that it advises not to perform a blind finger sweep of the mouth. I felt like something was guiding my hand as I did it anyway. I stuck my finger in the boy's mouth and pried out a large orange peel that was almost as big as my palm! I inserted my finger a second time and extracted a second piece of the peel from his throat.

And then it happened: he grunted and coughed; then he breathed! I watched life return as his cheeks gained color and his pulse resumed.

"Son, are you OK?!" I screamed.

"What's his name? What's his name?" I then yelled into the crowd.

The big man buckled to his knees.

"His name is Sam!"

"Sam, Sam, come on, man! Come on! Hang on! Hang with me! Can you hear me?" I pleaded.

There was no response.

I took my fist and rubbed my knuckles on his sternum. He stirred this time.

"Sam, can you hear me?"

He weakly nodded his head.

I looked at the big man, whom I now took to be his dad. His blue eyes locked with mine, and I reassured him, "He's gonna be all right. He's gonna be fine; I just know it!"

As we say in the South, Sam's dad "fell out" as hope appeared in our midst. He buckled to his knees and then lay face down in the hot grass, just crying. The crowd, which had grown to over a hundred people, surged and cheered as we all cried with joy. The ambulance arrived close to fifteen minutes later.

As I later learned, there were five families staying together in one beach house. The moms had all taken a spa day and the dads had been responsible for watching the kids. Sam, who reminded me of my boys with his blond hair and blue eyes, had fallen into the pool, and it had taken several minutes for anyone to notice. To this day, no one knows how that orange peel got stuck in his throat!

The owners of the house heard about Sam's story, and called to offer my family a free weeklong vacation at their beach house the next year. We were so moved. We visit DeBordieu every year, and each time, we ride by that house and reflect on that unforgettable day. I stare at that spot, and I can still see Sam lying on that green grass by the palmetto tree. Was it all a coincidence? I don't think so. There were way too many events that led me to be in that truck and by the side of that boy in less than a minute. What if the car Coker was driving had been working properly and we had gone straight to the golf course? What if I had gone to the grocery store with Kelliegh? What if we hadn't paid the boat fee? I believe the hand of God was present in those moments. It gives me chills to think about it. I believe *everything happens for a reason.*

\* \* \*

I'm Clay Lowder, and I'm a family doctor. I love medicine. These types of events seem to happen to me often, and I love to recount the stories.

Over the years, I have used stories such as Sam's to relate to my patients. I tell them my definition of true health. It's not just their medical history, but, instead, it's a blend of their physical, mental, **and** spiritual health. I even put that philosophy on the back of my first brochure when I started Lowder Family Practice twenty-two years ago in my hometown of Sumter, South Carolina. I love to help "guide" people to this life philosophy. My opinion is that life is short, and you only get one shot, so do it right!

> **My definition of true health is not just a patient's medical history but is a blend of their physical, mental, and spiritual health.**

I wrote this book as a vehicle to share these stories and my life philosophies with you. Jesus told stories. He used parables and let people draw their own conclusions. I hope you will read mine and reflect on each one. I want you to change. I want to energize you to take action to improve your health and your life. I want you to gain a positive outlook on life and see all that it has to offer. Lastly, I hope my book inspires you to see the "signs" that are all around us—the ones that guide us toward making certain choices.

In addition, I would like to give you some of what my wife calls "Lowderisms." They are phrases and other one-liners I received from great parents and teachers; some just came out of nowhere. I've repeated them so often that I frequently hear my kids using them. That reaffirmation makes me feel very good. I hope you will use and pass them along as you continue forward.

Here's an example: When I was in seventh grade at Wilson Hall in Sumter, my history teacher and football coach, Coach Faulkner, would grin and exclaim, "Never a dull moment, never a wasted second!" Forty years later, I'm still quoting Coach Faulkner and breathing life into others as he did for me. It became one of my first Lowderisms. In fact, I'm an assistant coach for my daughter's softball team, and I enthusiastically shout it regularly at her and her teammates during practice.

Liza even chose to use that particular Lowderism for her senior quote in the Wilson Hall yearbook. Coach Faulkner would certainly flash his big signature smile if he were to see the quote she chose, knowing I've passed on a nugget from his teaching days almost four decades ago.

I have a new motto now though, and I can't wait to tell you the story that inspired it.

I grew up a huge Clemson fan. My dad played baseball at Clemson University, and he began taking me to football games there when I was five years old. These days, I still go to almost every football game. Taking after my dad, I also graduated from Clemson University, and I carried on the fun by taking my children to games when they were just toddlers. We have not missed a season since. Our family loves to travel with the Tigers! It's become a tradition.

There is one game I remember vividly. Clemson was playing Auburn in Atlanta. It was the Chick-fil-A Kickoff Game in 2012 in the Georgia Dome. The Lowders were there, and we were excited. One of my two brothers, Dr. Milt Lowder, happens to be Clemson's sport psychologist. He has been an integral part of Clemson's success over the past ten years; just ask Coach Dabo Swinney! The team and coaches there have told me often how much they love Milt, and he has even passed multiple Lowderisms on to them.

Milt was the one who told me this story that inspired my next Lowderism: The night before the game in Atlanta, Dabo had a speaker come in to talk with the team to share some words of inspiration. This particular year, it was the world heavyweight champion, Evander Holyfield. His message was powerful. Hearing about his speech that night changed my life.

As Milt told it, the champ said, among other things, "Boys, you are winners by just being here in Atlanta. Winners travel! Losers sit at home. You are winners. Make sure you remember this as you go through life. Use it to motivate you and your families to become successful, and always travel. Go see things. Now, let's start by taking care of Auburn."

That they did; Clemson won 26–19!

"Winners travel." That was it. That was the motto I had been searching for. The minute I heard it, something went off in my brain. That phrase was my life, and more importantly, my life's work. It would go on to become my most loved Lowderism.

How does it work? What grabbed me? Well, in this book, I hope to show you, and that's why I chose it as the title to represent my thoughts. There are three parts to Winners Travel: mental, physical, and spiritual. All three parts must work together in order for you to experience a complete transformation.

Winners Travel is a way of life. It's a way to view life as a never-ending journey, always wanting to see new things and open your mind. It will drive you to explore and to be great.

**Mental:** I hope and pray Winners Travel will open your mind, and once your mind is open, it can never go back to the old way of thinking. This is freeing, which is the mental part of it. One of the best tricks that I have learned is to control my thoughts. How? It's called *displacement*. When you have a negative thought, you can learn to displace it by concentrating on a positive thought instead. Setting goals and planning trips is one of the ways I accomplish this. Your brain can be guided. It can be programmed to think of these things often, and doing so will relieve stress.

11

I'll show you how, and I'll provide stories of how Winners Travel to mental health.

**Physical:** Winners Travel to physical health as well. Of course, that's my specialty. I urge you to think about this. By the time most people come to see me (or any doctor), it's often too late.

Winners keep up with their physical health. I'll go over the latest technology and share with you how it will help you. Medicine has moved into the area of prevention, and I am a preventer. Many people visit doctors to try and reverse what's already been done rather than treating their problem before it becomes an even bigger one. The most important thing to remember (and something you can do right now, even if you don't read the rest of this book!) is to schedule a checkup! If you don't do it for yourself, do it for your family! Winners always think of others.

**Spiritual:** I believe this is the third aspect of Winners Travel. I witnessed Sam, the child who almost fatally drowned in the beginning of this book, come back to life. I saw him grin at me when we put him in that ambulance. I believe God has always guided my life, and that His guiding hand is the reason why memorable and inspirational moments happen to me.

We are on this earth for a deeper and more purposeful reason. I hope I can show you how to see the meaning of your time here every day. I hope and pray it changes your perspective and teaches you why you are here. I have many more miracles to share that have shown me how Winners Travel to spiritual health.

So let's get started on our journey. I thank you for letting me be your guide. I am so humbled by this opportunity to lead you, which I feel compelled to do. I'm excited to show you a new potential path. I believe everything happens for a reason—even your reading this book. Remember: Winners Travel to mental, physical, and spiritual health. If you observe this motto, it can change every aspect of your life.

Let's roll!

CHAPTER 2

# Championship of the World!

*"Always give 110 percent."*
— Clayton Lowder Jr.

M Y FATHER, CLAYTON LOWDER JR., was a catcher for Clemson University's baseball team. He was tough and he was good. Twice during his college career, he traveled to Omaha, Nebraska, to play in the College World Series. His Omaha stories are legendary. I think I inherited my storytelling ability from him.

My dad, whom I still call "Daddy" (I grew up calling him "Daddy" and still do to this day) says that his baseball coach, Coach Bill Wilhelm, looked at him during one of their visits to Omaha and said, "Little fella, go out there and catch the first pitch of the World Series. Take the ball and present it to Miss Omaha in the first row there."

Daddy said he looked around to see this good-looking blonde with a crown sitting in the front row. He ran to the dugout and grabbed another ball. He wrote on it, "Clayton Lowder, Days Inn, Room 35," and hid the ball in his mitt. After catching the first pitch, he ran over to her, winked, and handed her his ball.

"What happened, Daddy?" I always ask.

He claims proudly, "I got a date out of it!"

My daddy is a character. In his younger days, he was always up to something. He loves to tell stories, especially about how he pranked people. He even had a trick pen at his cotton gin, where he worked for about thirty years. He would open the cap and a fake mongoose would spring out, startling the unsuspecting visitor. The stunned prankee would run halfway across the county. My father claims he even pulled his infamous mongoose trick on Clemson's legendary football coach, Frank Howard. Oh, how he loves to tell that story!

My dad has Alzheimer's now, but he can still tell me the pitch count from one of those games in 1959 and doesn't easily forget the details about the many victims of the mongoose trap. I let him tell his entertaining stories to me over and over again.

My mother also has quite a story. As a young woman, she taught school in addition to being a full-time mother and housewife. Many years later, she earned her master's degree in English, followed by her PhD in philosophy: English, composition, and rhetoric. She is an amazing woman who now dedicates her life to teaching and mentoring students at the Medical University of South Carolina as the director of the Center for Academic Excellence and the Writing Center. She helps people all day, and I doubt there has been a student at the university over the past twenty years who hasn't benefited from her specialized tutoring and advising skills. She's practically *addicted* to helping these young people and has picked up the storytelling traits of my father and me; she tells colorful stories to her medical students to guide them through their dauntingly challenging days of professional school. Often, the stories she shares with her students are about me. My mama loves to tell her young aspiring physicians that I called her crying after receiving a score of 76 percent on my first two tests during my first year of medical school. (I dispute that!)

My parents have long understood the concept of Winners Travel, even before it was a phrase I used. We grew up on a farm, so we did not have much, but each summer, they took my siblings and me to Santee in South Carolina to stay in a musty trailer for two weeks. Looking back, it was magical. My brothers, Milt and Jim; my sister, Candler; and I loved it. We swam and fished, and my dad pulled us on a tractor inner tube connected to a small jonboat for hours each day. It was not much of a vacation, but it was ours, and I would not trade it for the world. While these trips may not sound luxurious (and they weren't!), they gave us time away from the stressors of work and school. The time away allowed us all to reconnect with one another and make memories that we still share years later.

My parents wanted more for us. They challenged us and pushed us, sometimes too much. They took us to Clemson games and signed us up to play all sports. The rule was that if we played a sport, we did not have to work, so, of course, we all played at least one sport!

They even took us out West one summer, although no, not by airplane. We drove there in a beat-up old camper that sat in the back of our daddy's pickup truck. Try to imagine three teenagers and a two-year-old stuck in the back of that thing as we traveled from the East Coast to the West Coast. I can still recall the smell of stinky feet in that camper!

But what a trip it was! We did not miss much. In Memphis, Tennessee, we stopped to visit the former home of Elvis Presley, whom my dad told us he had met once. After that, we went to Mount Rushmore, and then on to my favorite stop: Yellowstone National Park. We then traveled all the way to Yosemite by way of the Grand Canyon. It was a low budget, but that was the Lowder way. They instilled the Winners Travel mind-set in all of us kids.

Competition was also something that was bred into us Lowders. Everything was a game that allowed an opportunity to win. We would play the "Alphabet Game" or the "Spud Game," and the winner was typically rewarded with a milkshake.

My brother Milt and I always turned the competition up a notch. We had an extra dose of the "win at all costs" in us. We played one-on-one basketball, baseball, and even football on our farm. We had our own "Field of Dreams" in which we perfected our performance each day. I was older, so that made me the all-time referee. To add some pressure, we always shouted, "Ten seconds left!" at the end of each contest.

This meant that the battle was officially on. Every once in a while, Milt would accuse me of milking the clock in my favor, especially if I was taking the last shot. One of us had to lose, and whoever that was never took it too well.

"That wasn't right!" Milt would yell. "I have one second left!"

"No sir. It was fair and square. Face it: you choked!" I would poke back.

"OK, best two out of three!"

And the second game was on.

I'll admit it: Lowders are not the greatest losers.

Finally, when I was exhausted, I would declare, "This is for the championship of the world!" which meant, "This is it! Last game. Period." Whoever won was the champion. At least for that day.

Yet another reason why the phrase Winners Travel had such an impact on me. It is my life story. My wife tells me I have "another gear." I have always been driven to succeed and lead a meaningful, strong life. I have made life my own competition, and I love it. Each phase of my life has been "for the championship of the world!"

Whether it is doctoring, coaching my kids, being intentional in my marriage, or even fishing, I set goals and then make plans to win. I know that sometimes it can be too much, but I would rather go after something than nothing at all. I have decided that Winners Travel is my life! I want to live a determined life and reap all the benefits of that, and I am motivated to tell everyone I know the secret to doing so. I have instilled this mind-set in my kids, Clayton, Coker, and Liza. My wife, Kelliegh, also bought in. She even designed personalized luggage tags for our bags that say, "Winners Travel."

I tell them, "It is more than a trip or an expensive vacation. It is a way of life; it is your *game plan* for life!"

They sometimes sigh and roll their eyes when I am preaching, but I persist.

When Liza was a freshman at Clemson University (yup, she followed in the footsteps of her father and grandfather!), she once brought home five of her friends from college, and we all went to DeBordieu together. It was a magical weekend. One of the highlights was that Clemson's football Coach, Dabo Swinney, had rented the house next to us for the weekend. We were all starstruck when we met him on the beach. They were so kind that we invited them to stop by our house any time, but we didn't think they would come by *that night* (they had a wedding rehearsal dinner to go to). But he actually came over later with his family! They were incredibly warm and funny; we were so comfortable together that it felt like we had been friends for years. We even battled on our orange pool table till the wee hours of the morning. After visiting with him, I realized he has the Winners Travel motto down. He even FaceTimed my brother, and grilled him as to why he wasn't there spending time with us. When my brother gave some lame excuse, Dabo yelled at him, "Winners Travel, man!"

However, the best part of the trip came later. Liza asked that Kelliegh and I have dinner one of the nights with her and her friends, so after they picked the restaurant, we did just that.

Dinner began with small talk. We didn't know most of the girls, so we asked the usual questions. Then we got down to business. I was so proud of Liza as she led the way.

"Dad, please tell them about the book you're writing."

I love having opportunities to share with young kids how to have a Winners Travel mentality, and encourage them about their futures.

I quickly went through my story and moved on to the deeper questions. We started with Liza and went around the table.

Question one was: "What's your biggest strength?" It took a little coaxing, but we teased answers out of them.

Question two was tougher: "What's your biggest weakness?" They were scared to say much, so I went first. This relaxed them and reminded them that *everybody* has a weakness and that it's OK not to be perfect. Soon, they laughed and began to roll out what they saw as their own weaknesses.

## Where do you see yourself in ten years?

The final question was the big one. I use it with almost all the teenagers I see as patients: "Where do you see yourself in ten years?"

We pried out all the nitty-gritty details on this one: "What does your future spouse look like? What's your job? What is your spouse's job? Where do you live—the country *and* the city? How much money do you make? Where do you want to travel to? What do you want to see in your life? How many kids will you have? What type of church will you attend? What relationships do you desire? Why?"

Well, those girls rocked it. We sat there for two hours as they poured their hearts out. Liza, Juls, Arlena, Mary Crosby, Emily, and Sage laid out a game plan to live their lives mentally, physically, and spiritually.

Our restaurant server overheard the conversation and approached us afterward.

She said, "I've heard a lot of things over the years while doing this job, but your girls were saying all the right stuff. I was blown away by the words of these young people."

The girls blushed. I swooned. Needless to say, she got a Ben Franklin for a tip!

Now that's how you do it. That's a Winners Travel dinner. I feel confident that those girls are set on a path that will guide their lives; they have a road map. They were already great and driven young ladies, but they left that night with a more vivid plan in their minds.

All of those girls have written me since that night, thanking my wife and me for the dinner and conversation. (By the way, thank-you notes are one way that Winners put others first. I suggest you write them regularly. They are almost better for the person writing them than the one receiving them.)

After seeing the transformation this dinner had for Liza and her friends, I believe that everybody should schedule a Winners Travel dinner with their family. All you have to do is ask the three questions I mentioned above. Encourage your family to dream big. Plan the dinner now.

> **Planning things out is just another way Winners Travel allows for the most successful mental, physical, and spiritual transformation.**

Planning things out is just another way Winners Travel allows for the most successful mental, physical, and spiritual transformation. Your brain is wired to respond to these plans and will subconsciously work toward achieving those goals. But, sometimes it backfires and gets stuck on negative things. Over the years, I have learned to trick it out of the negativity trap. How? By writing down my goals and reading them daily. My thoughts may drift as I get stressed, but my mind will always return its focus to my long-term goals and dreams if I have them written down. It makes my daily grind more tolerable and continues to give me perspective. Writing down your goals will help you remember what it is you're reaching for and what you need to do to get there.

I love to share Winners Travel and goal-setting with my patients. I feel the Winners Travel motto works for most of my patients who have anxiety and depression. I have learned that if I am going to really help them, I have to offer more than a prescription to pills; I need to give them perspective. I have to challenge them to live this short life in a better way and get them engaged mentally, spiritually, and physically.

So I challenge you too. As I have said, Winners Travel is a way of life.

My family has shaped me into the man and doctor I am today. You can help shape yourself and your family as well.

Remember, "It's for the championship of the world!"

# CHAPTER 3

# Run Everywhere You Go!

*"My name is Sue! How do you do?"*
— Johnny Cash

NOW THAT WE HAVE A game plan for the future, I want to tell you about my past. This story is meant to motivate you.

I grew up on a farm, but I got out of that way of life. Here is why:

Imagine yourself standing in the middle of a cotton field. It is July in South Carolina. It's sticky, hot, and dry—and I mean *hot!* I can still feel the sun beating down on my back. One year it was over one hundred degrees Fahrenheit for ten days straight.

My job title for the summer was head pigweed puller. My dad grew cotton, but it seemed like he had more pigweed in the fields. I ran a crew, and we pulled all day long. Did I mention that it was hot? The pay wasn't exactly great either: one dollar an hour!

Pigweed is an interesting plant. It's sticky, has a distinct odor, and has tiny burrs that get all over you. Shorts are not an option for the weed puller, as its blackish-red berries tend to smear all over you. Oh yeah, and Mr. Pigweed has a root. It digs in, and when you go to pull it up, it pulls back. You have to work it back and forth to get it to let go. Then, after all that work, it is on to the next one—and there were *thousands* of them. I am telling you, that task is the number one reason I am a doctor!

"Is this farming?" I would ask my dad over and over.

"Yes, son that's it."

"Oh boy, well, if that's all there is to it, I want out!"

My dad would grin. He knew good and well what he was doing. All of the Lowders had been farmers, and he knew it would likely be in my blood.

"Please, Daddy, let me drive the tractor! Let me run the store! Please, anything but that field!" I would plead.

"No sir, son. I need you on that crew."

My brother, Milt, and I were together the other day and began reminiscing about those days. My brother brought it up first: "Remember when we'd be pulling weeds and you would

28

get in the truck? You would say, 'Hey! I hear the radio going off; I'm going to see if Daddy wants me.' You would run to the truck and grab the shortwave radio, and tell the crew, 'Hey, my dad needs me to pick up a part for him.' Then you would take off and come back thirty minutes or so later."

It did not take my brother long to figure out how to take a break. Every time after that, he would jump in the truck with me. The rest of the crew never caught on.

My dad loved Johnny Cash. He could not sing a lick, but he tried. His all-time favorite song was "A Boy Named Sue," which I had memorized. In the song, "Sue" finally catches up with his dad, who had left the family when Sue was young. The grown boy tears into his father in a barroom brawl. When he goes to kill him, his dad stops him and says, "Son, this world is rough, and if a man's gonna make it, he's gotta be tough."

The boy stops. He thinks maybe ole dad was right: *I have made it. I am tough.* Then the song continues from the boy's standpoint: "And I came away with a different point of view."

I love that part because it hits home with me. My dad was diagnosed with Alzheimer's disease years ago. He has been out of it since then, and he was not there to help me along.

Looking back, maybe that is why he made me pull weeds so much. He knew then that I needed some "gravel in my guts and spit in my eye." Now, when I pause to think about it, I realize I'm grateful. I'm thankful for those brutal summer days in that field. The tough-love lessons he taught me have made all the difference as I shaped my career and future.

So Parenting 101 could also be called Farming 101. The first lesson is, "Make your kids work." I have interviewed many successful people, and they all have a story. It usually involves a remedial task they had to do while growing up. Though they hated it at the time, it taught them a lot about life. They know how to hustle now. Hard work makes a winner.

Most parents today do just the opposite. They want their kids to grow up with a different life than they had. They try to smooth everything out for them. I did it with my own kids; I provided and rescued them from adversity over and over again. If I learned one thing, it was that if my kids were going to be Winners Travel people, I needed to make them work harder and let them fail more often.

Think about it: let your kids fail over and over. It sure hurts, but handing over a success without requiring work to be done will backfire. Why deny your kids the very opportunity that made you great?

I would like to challenge you to give them this opportunity. Give them a remedial task right now. It can be something as simple as being in charge of the laundry or raking leaves. As members of the family, they are required to do it. I can just hear them complaining now, but, hey, it will be good for them! Stick to it. Let them work for their results, and then ask them how they feel once they've completed it. I guarantee they will feel validated and stronger as an individual.

My mom was also in on the gig growing up. We had a Black Bart stove in our kitchen, and my brother and I were responsible for keeping the woodpile well stocked during the winter. Mama would not let us put the woodpile by the house. Oh no, it had to be one hundred yards away, near the swamp. Milt and I lugged a wheelbarrow each morning at 6:00 a.m. to retrieve wood, and then we built a fire in the Black Bart stove to warm the kitchen. I can still see that wheelbarrow. It was yellow, but the metal was rusted and the blend of colors was the ugliest hue you've ever seen. The wheelbarrow was largely broken; the wheel would often go flat or the handle would sometimes tilt, and all the logs would fall out. Milt would yell at me, and I'd yell back, and the fight was on. Despite that, we would eventually get the job done. I should note that we did not even need the heat from the fire since we had central heating in our home. It was just another remedial task.

Oh, and let me tell you about the piano. My mom was determined to make us "cultural" by making us learn to play an instrument. She was not going to just let us be farmers. Here is how that conversation went:

I played in a piano guild one day (at least, I think they called it that), and when I finished, I sat back down and whispered, "Mama, how'd I do?"

"It was . . . good, son." She turned her head away as she mumbled this, but I still noticed that her face was red. "You only missed a few notes."

While I had been forced to take piano for five years, I was completely tone deaf. I could not hear, play, or feel the music. I say it's bad genetics. However, my mom was relentless.

"Clay, you will regret it one day if you cannot play the piano for your friends."

"But they laugh at me now!" I protested.

Finally, she gave in and let me exit the music world after sticking with it for so long. Well, I still sing, but only in private. My mom and dad knew the value of a remedial task, and it taught us well.

The lesson for Winners Travel is clear: in order to develop inner strength and true character, you must first learn to do things you just don't want to do. The best way to teach this lesson to your kids is to simply make them do things they don't want to do. Delayed gratification is good for them. Heck, it's good for you too! If you want something big in your future, chances are, you will have to give up something today to get it. That's a traveling mind-set.

When your kids are doing their tasks, they will balk and maybe revolt, but years later, they will thank you. While writing this book, my Uncle Jimmy passed away, and I delivered the eulogy at his funeral. Uncle Jimmy was passionate about raising a lot of things: coon dogs, raccoons, and even crows. However, he was most dedicated to raising his three girls: Ansley, Rhett, and Nancy Hunter. I learned much from him and my parents, most importantly: Be intentional about raising your kids—and by intentional, I mean put in persistent effort. Develop a plan and stick to it, no matter what.

> **The lesson for Winners Travel is clear: in order to develop inner strength and true character, you must first learn to do things you just don't want to do.**

Eulogizing Jimmy brought back a flood of memories for me. My dad had made us all work at Lowder Brothers Gin Company, the company he owned with his brother Jimmy. My dad was tough, one of the toughest men I knew. He would start work early and stay late. He and my Uncle Jimmy made it happen in both farming and ginning cotton. My hat is off to them. They put all of us through college. How? Persistent effort. They stuck with it in good years and bad. They could outwork anybody. They flat-out hustled.

That hustle that they exemplified is the number one thing they taught me. I can remember trying to keep up with my dad while walking down a cotton row. His walk required me to run. He even walked that fast to church. Now, I run almost everywhere I go. I go hard. It is another Lowderism, and I preach it to my kids.

As I write this, I have just returned from Sumter Mall, where I was buying my kids some books for Easter. The parking lot was almost full, so I had to park near the end of a row. I literally ran to the front entrance. People were staring at me, but I didn't care; I'm used to it. It's good, brief exercise and it wakes me up and gives me energy.

Later in this book, I will talk more about physical health and why these short bursts of hustle are better than an hour of running. You should give it a try. If you feel funny, just try fast walking to begin with. It will put a little pep in your step. Besides, it's fun to watch people's faces as you bustle past them!

Remember, it is never too late to get started on a new way of life. That's one of the fundamental precepts of Winners Travel. Even if you did not have a childhood of work and sweat, it is OK to start today with your kids or grandkids. Be intentional. Think of Farming 101 as a base for them. Get out there, and show them how to hustle.

Show them how to run everywhere they go! It will make all the difference.

# CHAPTER 4

# The Farmer–Doctor

*"There is still time on the clock!"*
— Deshaun Watson

MY DECISION TO BECOME A doctor was largely shaped by illnesses in my family. My dad is a Type 1 diabetic, and he has needed insulin shots daily since age twenty-seven just to live. Because he was constantly "grinding," he would often run his blood sugar so low that he would act drunk. He has even gotten into car accidents before as a result of his blood sugar dropping too low. In one particular accident, he flipped his big spreader truck three times on a busy highway. The Lord was definitely looking out for him because thankfully, he was not seriously injured.

My mom would cook my dad three meals a day; he was "low carb" back when it wasn't even cool! Because my dad has needed insulin shots for more than half of his life—I can't remember him without them—I have also always been involved in his care. I was the one responsible for bringing him a Snickers bar or orange juice whenever I noticed his blood sugar dropping.

Fifty years later, he has had very few long-term complications. This has shown me firsthand how a stringent watch over diabetes matters, and I push my patients to maintain that control. Helping my dad was my first taste of what it was like to help people take control of their health and live a rich and full life despite their diagnosis.

Another disease that has impacted my family and me is Parkinson's disease. My grandmother on my mother's side, Jane Ariail, had a severe case. She had to be admitted into a local nursing home for years until her heartbreaking death. My mama was her caretaker, and she went to visit her mama (my grandmama) every day. She was in charge of my grandmother's health—physical, mental, and spiritual. She took it seriously, and boy, what a task it was!

After my grandmother had a tracheotomy tube inserted in her windpipe so she could breathe, my mother cleaned it out when it filled with mucus, and she turned her every two hours to prevent bed sores. It was almost impossible to communicate with my grandmother because of her trach tube, but her brain activity was normal, so we could see how frustrating it was for her to know what she wanted to say and how to say it but remain unable to. My mother got creative and made her a keyboard using Scrabble tiles glued onto a poster. My grandmother would painstakingly point to one letter at a time to spell out words, but my mom's patience never wavered.

My mom made sure my grandmother's mental health stayed strong as well. She always brought her fresh flowers to keep her room fresh and lively, and she read to her during every visit. Most importantly, she would make the rest of the family go visit her. To tell you the truth, we kids really did not want to go. It smelled; sorry to be so blunt, but it just stank in my grandmother's facility. On top of that, most of the people wandering the halls yelled and grabbed at us, which made us really uncomfortable. I didn't understand it back then, but I get it now. Our visits were more for our grandmother than for us; she needed the familiarity and love of her family.

In addition to all of that, my mother took care of my grandmother's spiritual needs. She would read *Guideposts* magazine and the family Bible to her. James was her favorite book of the Bible because it was a story of hope and thanks. I am not sure how she did it, but my grandmother seemed to grow even stronger in her faith because of these simple acts by my mother.

See? Even back then, my family lived by the "Winner's Travel" mentality. It should always remain a priority to take care of your physical, mental, and spiritual needs; it can get you through the toughest of times, even when the outlook is grim.

With everything that happened with my grandmother, I saw my mom's dedication, but I also saw a lot of suffering and pain. I wondered if my mother felt like she had a support system, and I remember thinking that there had to be a better way to go about life.

So, at an early age, I decided that I was going to be a doctor so that I could change the lives of people like my grandmother, mother, and father. I wanted to help people like my grandmother and mother—the patient and the dedicated caretaker. I wanted to help people like my father, who had to adjust their path and learn to live with a medical illness that would require constant attention, care, and medicine, Lastly, I was confident that I could find new and innovative approaches to help patients and caretakers. I was excited, and I set a plan in my mind to go and do it. But my path to get there wasn't easy. The people in my town sure didn't think I could do it. They would frequently tell me that I just *couldn't*. They said I wasn't smart enough or that I wasn't sophisticated enough; I was just a farmer redneck.

I remember even my baseball coach once telling me, "Lowder, you are so dumb, you can't even steal second base. There is no way you are going to be a doctor."

For me, comments like those just added fuel to my fire. I wanted to show everybody how wrong they were. *Game on,* I would respond in my head when I heard them say those things. I ran even harder everywhere I went because now I had something to prove. Why is that? I have reflected on that question a lot. What is it about negativity that can drive somebody to do more and more?

Remember in grade school when another kid dared you to do something? Or when your friends said they didn't believe that you could accomplish a certain task? Most of us respond by doing *anything* to prove that we can do exactly what we said we could. We often hear celebrities give shout-outs to their "haters." Why? I believe that when you set a goal to prove how capable you are, to yourself *and* to others, negative feedback can either be a ball and chain attached to your ankle or the wind behind your sails. Remember to harness that feedback, and let it drive you through every decision. One day, you'll be able to look back at how far you've come and how you've grown—all thanks to your "haters."

> **When you set a goal to prove how capable you are, to yourself *and* to others, negative feedback can either be a ball and chain attached to your ankle or the wind behind your sails.**

You've probably heard the story about Winston Churchill and the shortest graduation speech ever given. As the story goes, he said, "Never, never, never give up!" And then he sat down. Now, I've heard it's not totally true, but I still repeat those words over and over. I think Babe Ruth also said something that goes perfectly with what I'm arguing. He said, "You just can't beat the person who never gives up."

So I persisted, and eventually I became a physician. Years into my practice, I was also able to found the Winner's Travel Foundation, which recognizes caretakers of those with ailments. I hope that with my foundation I can shed light on those who sacrifice so much of their time and dedicate every moment of their day to help others. I look back at the goals I laid out for myself when I was much younger: help patients live healthy lives, and honor the lives of caretakers. I am proud to say I've been able to do both.

However, it wasn't as simple as my waking up one day and saying, "Today, I'm going to be a doctor." No, I had to set (and reset . . . and reset) goals and actively work toward them every single day. Goal-setting has always been a part of my life, and especially so when I decided on my career path. When I told everyone that I was going to be a doctor, I *knew* I was going to do it. At age ten, when I told my parents that I was going to Clemson, I *meant* it. How did I know it? It all goes back to goal-setting and that persistence I mentioned earlier. I knew that when I would set my sights on a goal, I would carefully plan and calculate every step along the way that I needed to take in order to reach the finish line and accomplish it. I knew that I would find a way to get the end result I wanted.

One of the stops on my path toward becoming a doctor was attending Clemson University—a big university in a small town. It was originally a land-grant university, perfect for me, a farmer-doctor! I even took some agriculture classes to honor my dad and stay in touch with my "roots." Interestingly enough, I struggled more with those classes than the premed ones!

At Clemson, I was president of the Kappa Sigma fraternity, which opened up the opportunity for me to organize travel outside of our small university town. I was able to coordinate road trips all over to see our team, the Tigers, play. I watched us beat Penn State and Oklahoma State in back-to-back years in bowl games, and I cheered on Danny Ford as their coach. He led us to three straight 10-2 records while I was studying at Clemson. Today, all three of my kids go to Clemson. I'm happy to keep the tradition going.

After I graduated from Clemson, I attended medical school in Columbia, South Carolina (my daddy would never let me say, "USC" or "University of South Carolina"). Then I decided that I wanted to change things up a bit and get a little more "cultured," so I went on to do my residency in a bit bigger of a town: downtown Charlotte, North Carolina.

Once there, my path to becoming a physician wasn't as clear as I thought it would be, and there were some bumps in the road. To put it simply, I started to become unsure of what I wanted. I said, "I'm going to be a cardiologist!" when studying cardiology, and "I'm going to be an orthopedist!" when learning orthopedics. My best friend in medical school, James Goodson, was going into ophthalmology, and I was impressed by yet another career path. It didn't help matters that all of these fancy professions were accompanied by visions of dollar signs!

I maintained strong grades, so most of my friends and mentors said, "Clay, you must specialize!" But I wasn't ready to do that yet. I was interested in everything, still a little confused on what to declare, and I wanted to be sure I made the right choice. I was getting nervous that I hadn't decided yet, but when I mentioned to one of my mentors, Dr. Jim Stallworth, that I needed to decide as soon as possible, he stopped me in my tracks. He said to me, "No way and I will tell you why." He was one of the brightest pediatricians I'd ever met, so I respected his guidance.

His story recalled a very specific day during my third year, when all students had to bring an unusual patient case to what is called "Grand Rounds." At "Grand Rounds," we were asked to explain the details of these unusual cases to a group of doctors, who would then grill us and review our recommended treatment plans. It was intimidating; I had to present my findings in front of the entire pediatric department. They smirked as I spoke and then shot daggers at me with their judgmental eyes. Everything went south after I explained that I'd ordered a certain lab test. I tried to support my stance, but one of the doctors smoked me for it. My ship was sinking fast. I began to think back to my baseball coach's words so long ago. *Was he right?! Was I too dumb to be a doctor?*

Then it happened. A strong voice boomed from the back of the room.

"I'd have done exactly what Dr. Lowder did! In fact, I did it many times in my career!"

I looked closer and spotted my childhood hero and personal pediatrician, Dr. "Pap" Propst. He walked to the front of the room, stood beside me, and put the doctors in their places.

"Yeah," I said to myself. Then louder, for the other doctors to hear me, I said, "What he said. Any more questions?"

Dr. Propst was a legend in South Carolina. He had practiced medicine for forty years, and many considered him the absolute best in the biz. Now here he was—standing up for me. I puffed out my chest, and he winked at me as I strode out of the room.

After reminding me of this story, Dr. Jim Stallworth went back to his advice regarding specialization: "Clay, you have a primary care personality. You cannot specialize in orthopedics.

Hell, you can't even spell *appetite,* much less *ophthalmology.*"
(He was right; I had misspelled both of those words in one of
my papers. He even told that to the crowd at my graduation
ceremony.)

"You have a burden to carry. You have to do family medicine
or pediatrics." He told me I would be lonely if I specialized and
that I should stick to my roots. He understood my personality
and knew I had grown up on a farm. He said that I had a
responsibility to take care of "my people."

Well, my goose was cooked. For a while, those words
haunted me. I prayed. I even sulked. *There goes the money,
the fame, the future. I am doomed!* I thought. But, the next
rotation sealed the deal for a specialization: ophthalmology.
And guess what? I was so dad-gummed bored after one week.

"Better one or better two?" I would ask the patients over
and over again as I clicked through the different lens options in
front of their face as they stared at an eye chart in the distance.

"Well, I don't know Doctor," they would squint and say
repeatedly.

"Just pick one, lady!" I would bellow in frustration.

One day, I called Kelliegh (my girlfriend at the time). I
started whispering to her.

"What in the world are you doing?" she asked.

"Shhh!" I softly hissed, "I'm in the closet hiding. I can't go out there anymore!"

That was that. Ophthalmology was out!

My mind was still racing back to primary care and what Dr. Stallworth had said to me. So, for my next rotation, I signed up for family medicine. Of all the cities where I could apply, I picked tiny Prosperity, South Carolina, because a South Carolina legend, Dr. Oscar Lovelace, was there. I had heard him speak before, and I thought he was brilliant; I wanted to follow in his footsteps. He said he would take chickens, and even eggs, as a form of payment! On top of that, he was always continuing to better himself. At the time I heard him speak, he was going back to school to add C-sections to his long list of medical experience.

Best of all, he loved his patients. It was clear that he loved family medicine as well. He knew all of his patients by their first name, and they absolutely adored him. He was educated and eloquent, both as a speaker and as a doctor, but he was "country" too! Seeing Dr. Lovelace speak and then being able to complete a rotation in his small hometown was when things turned around for me. I finally understood what I needed to set my sights on in terms of my medical profession, and my goals became much clearer. My broad goal to become a doctor became much more finely tuned: I wanted to go into primary care. I remember thinking to myself, *Yes, Clay, you* can *have it all!* And boy did I want it. After my rotation in Prosperity, my path was set. I chose family practice, and it has made all the difference. Not only have I been able to achieve my goals of working in medicine and being able to make a difference in the lives of the people who need it most, but I have been able to do so in a field that allows me to give back to my community and stick to my "farmer" roots.

Farming is still a big part of me. As you'll read later on, I own a farm, and I am still learning lessons of hard work from the farm life. I can't drive past a cotton field without being transported back to my childhood and those hot summer days. Many of my patients are farmers too, and I do everything I can to help them make the right decisions regarding their health so that they can continue to live a long life on their farm.

I also fell in love with my high school sweetheart and fellow farm girl, Kelliegh Waynick. We always dreamed of a life together on a farm—one complete with horses, cows, dogs, you name it. You could say we started the concept of Winners Travel way back then! Our romance started while traveling in the back of the Wilson Hall bus. *Oh, stop it, Clay; this is a clean book!*

Kelliegh's father and mother, Harold and Gail, were great Christian parents and role models in the community. Before Kelliegh and I got to know each other, her parents suggested to her that she and her then boyfriend were getting too serious, and they wanted them to break up for a time to allow themselves to focus on other things. I was going through a breakup of my own; my girlfriend had been secretly seeing other guys.

When my girlfriend told me it was over, I was crushed. I knew she would have no problem finding someone to date, but what about me? She actually suggested I get to know Kelliegh Waynick. I didn't know Kelliegh well at the time, but I was aware that she was a cheerleader and had recently won the title of "Miss Baron." She was so out of my league! Nevertheless, I decided that I wanted to date her. I told my boys—Westy Bowen, Andy Fort, and Joey Turbeville—that Kelliegh would be my next girlfriend. They just laughed at me. But I'm intentional right?

Back to the Wilson Hall bus ride. We were riding the bus home from a game against Williamsburg Academy. Kelliegh and her friend Aline were just one row ahead of me, and I was listening carefully to their conversation. They were going on and on about how much they loved Polo cologne. It came in a dark-green bottle with a gold top, and it was *the* cologne to have as a teenaged male. Since I just so happened to keep some in my travel bag, I subtly leaned down in my seat and shuffled through my bag to retrieve it. But when I went to open the bottle, something happened: I dropped it. So much for trying to be smooth! The bus was so loud as it rattled down the street that no one heard the bottle crack, but soon, the fruity scent of that cheap cologne filled the back of the bus. That smell, when mixed with that of sweaty boys, was far less than pleasant.

Soon, everyone could smell it. I was too embarrassed to fess up, so I played along.

"Oh my gosh! Who did that?!" I exclaimed and pinched my nose.

Aline left her seat for a minute—maybe to get away from the smell—and I finally had my chance. So I dove in and introduced myself to Kelliegh. I mainly just listened as she told me her story of heartbreak.

I didn't make a move that night. Instead, I decided that I would just be her friend and a shoulder to cry on. It worked. Slowly but surely, I went from being a friend to being her boyfriend, and the rest is history. I married my cheerleader and high school sweetheart; take that, boys!

When Kelliegh and I started dating, we would have long, serious talks about our future goals. Turns out, we had a lot in common; we dreamed big while keeping to our farming upbringing. We both wanted to live in Sumter, in the country. We loved antebellum estates of the Deep South, and we would draw our house and farm with colored pencils and magic markers. We wanted horses and chickens. We wanted to live on a pond. The list went on. So we made a goal for our future lives together, and kept it at the forefront of our minds.

Now, I'm a farmer-doctor. I thank God for helping me find a way to do two things that I love. While I knew at a young age that I didn't want to work on a farm, I always knew that farming would be a hobby of mine. But farming is the best way to lose money, so it pays to have my doctoring to fuel my hobby.

Don't worry though, I have a farm manager—Bryan Caughman—who really runs the show on our farm. Bryan has been a huge blessing in my life. He's the best young farmer I know, and he has one of the best attributes that I don't: he is patient. This is a trait that the Lowder men—I, especially—just don't have. When I decide on something, I tend to go full steam ahead to make it happen; I am not very good at sitting and waiting. Bryan has taught me to have a little bit of patience in everything I do.

My other man is Willie Wilson and his wife, Pat. Willie farmed for my father for as long as I can remember, and he now farms for me. He and Pat are part of our family. In fact, we even moved them across the road from us! Willie has a great personality and wit like no other; he's always smiling and laughing. I've learned from him too. He's shown me to put some care into everything I do rather than to just get things done quickly. He cringes when I get on the tractor because I usually tear something up within five minutes. My type A personality doesn't go well with tractor driving. He just laughs when I do this and understands that I'm trying my best out there!

Some of my first life lessons of hard work were learned on my daddy's farm, and even now as I own my own farm, I am constantly learning, but I love the farm life. I love having my friends and family come and enjoy the country with my family and me. I actually bought my dad's farm from him, and one of the first things I did was plant a huge dove field. My dad loved dove hunting, and growing up, I remember that he would ask people from all over to hunt and fellowship. I'm proud to carry on that Lowder tradition. Some of my best friends and I get together each Wednesday and enjoy what my friends call "The Ultimate Dove Club." Some who come over—like Whit Player, Roby Kelley, Freddie Edmunds, and Brian Scott—are lifelong friends in addition to hunting partners. Just don't ever miss a bird around them; you won't hear the end of it!

It's funny now to look back and think that at one point, I had never even considered being a family doctor; I feel as if my whole life was preparing me to become just that. The "farm" in me helps me to relate to many of my patients. I love being considered a "country doctor." I still make house calls, and I think that growing up on a farm gives me a unique set of experiences that allow me to understand what life is like out there. Being a farmer is hard, taxing labor, and you don't often rest. If your farm isn't running, you're likely not turning any profits. I understand that life because I watched my father live it, and I even lived it up until I left to go to medical school. On top of that, coming from a family that valued time spent together helped me to understand how important it is to help others live up to their full potential—physically, mentally, and spiritually. I am thankful for the moments in my past and the people who have shaped me into who I am today.

Reflecting on the moments from your past that shaped you is a part of a Winners Travel mind-set. Think back to your own childhood. Are there certain moments that stand out? Were there certain tasks you had to do? What made you great? Did anyone ever say you could not do things? Did anyone say you were "too dumb"? Were there people who doubted you?

> **Reflecting on the moments from your past that shaped you is a part of a Winners Travel mind-set.**

Stop right now, and write everything down. Yes, all of it—the good and the bad. Putting pen to paper and getting everything out is therapy for the soul. It will open your mind. Yes, some of it may not be good, but remember, you do not know how good winning is until you have lost. You do not know good until you have had bad!

As Deshaun Watson said during the national championship game versus Alabama when he saw he had just two minutes left, "There is still time on the clock!"

# CHAPTER 5

# Top Five

*"You become the top five people you hang out with."*
— Clay Lowder

IF YOU WANT TO BE the best at anything, you will have to play the game with people better than you. My children learned this lesson early on because they were so involved in sports.

When my son Coker was ten years old, we got him golf lessons from one of the best players of the game, George Bryan. Coker would go on trips with the Bryan family and play rounds with his sons, George Bryan IV and Wesley Bryan. Both are professional golfers now, and Wesley has even won on the PGA Tour! It was amazing to watch how much my ten-year-old's game improved when he played with college golfers! Coker went on to become a back-to-back state champion golfer and made the all-state team.

Clayton, my oldest son, had a similar experience. He wanted to become a professional bass fisherman, so he went with the best—me! (I am just kidding.) He went fishing with and against the best in South Carolina, people like Jon Smoak, Buddy Holmes, and touring pro Andy Montgomery. Clayton became a skilled angler, and won the junior championship for high school students. He then went on to represent South Carolina in his age division at the Bass Federation Championship of Bass Fishing!

Liza, my darling daughter, played varsity softball in the eighth grade. When she was just thirteen, she actually slid into home in extra innings, causing her team to win the state championship! She improved quickly by playing with older girls. In her senior year, she had monster hits in back-to-back games to first tie, then win the state championship again. It was certainly a magical moment for her and her dad.

That same year, I was asked to be an assistant coach for Liza's softball team at her high school, Wilson Hall. It was an honor to have been asked. In just a little under one season, I learned so much from the two team coaches, Teresa Alexander and Kristall Hanson. They used a combination of discipline and love to get the girls to peak performance and eventually win the 2018 state title. Even though those two coaches were much younger than I, they were far beyond my years in coaching. Their primary goal was always "to build young women." Winning softball games came second. They would take time out of practice to discuss with the girls the psychology of winning. One thing they would have their girls do, for example, was write their goals on their mirrors at home. They taught them about the power of positive reinforcement and how it can dictate their day from start to finish. The coaches also reminded the girls what it can do for not only themselves as individuals, but also for their fellow teammates when they give praise and celebrate even the tiniest of victories (like remembering to bring one's batting glove to practice!). They helped me learn to see "beyond the game," and grow into the role of a confident coach.

I have done a lot in my life, but watching my girls win state the year that I coached is one of my best memories. I became so attached to all of those girls! They even had a nickname for me: "HBC," which stood for "head ball coach."

One night, I had dinner with my daughter, Liza, and two of her teammates, Drake and Kathryn, who were other senior leaders on the team. At this dinner, I told them the story of Winners Travel, and they loved it. Drake even put it as her senior quote in the yearbook and took it a step further by writing, "Winners Travel; Losers Stay at Home." I made it into that yearbook twice—once as assistant coach and once as a senior-quote inspiration! Boy, was I feeling blessed that year!

That was the first Winners Travel dinner. I asked them each about their goals and aspirations. We talked about dreams they had for their futures. We plotted out their lives and set milestones that they could achieve along the way to their main goals. The girls loved it, we even cried together at that table. What started out as a conversation to develop a game plan to win state that year turned into developing a game plan for the rest of their lives. To this day, those girls still call and text me to share their big and little wins as they continue forward on the path they set out for themselves. This served as yet another affirmation for me that I should spend the rest of my life helping people learn how to live a mentally, physically, and spiritually healthy life.

Thanks to Coach Alexander, Coach Hanson, and the girls from the dinner, I realized that my time spent coaching did not only make me a better coach, but also a better father and doctor. I wasn't the one doing the coaching; they all coached *me*. I am a pretty emotional guy, and I cried more tears of joy that year than any other. Everyone wants a guide, but everyone *needs* a coach. Sometimes you get coached the most by the very people you are helping.

The idea that you should surround yourself with the best doesn't just apply to sports. You'll often hear people say that they don't want to be the smartest one in the room, and I am firm in my belief that that is 100 percent true. If you want to grow, *really* grow, you have to recognize that there will always be somebody out there who knows more than you, can do ABC task better than you, is stronger than you, etc.

This not only keeps you humble and receptive to learning, but also it reminds you to appreciate each and every person's unique "gift" to this world. I could have looked at the coaches or the girls on the team, seen how much younger they were than I, and dismissed them, thinking they didn't have enough "life experience" to help me. But instead, I turned to them and became their student;

**Everyone wants a guide, but everyone *needs* a coach. Sometimes you get coached the most by the very people you are helping.**

I wanted to learn everything they had to offer, because I knew that it would make me a better person. Everybody has something to offer you; you just have to listen and watch for it.

After the dinner I mentioned earlier, I stressed to my girls that they identify the top five individuals they should hang out with and then strive to become like those people. It's true. If you want to change your life, pick five Winners you know, and go hang out with them. Ask them to lunch. Ask them questions: What's their biggest strength? What's their biggest weakness? If they had to do it all over again, what would they change? What's the coolest place they've ever been to? In theory, it seems pretty simple, right? But it can be hard to identify those people. Be selective, and try to mix it up. This is a task we can all accomplish but we seldom do. Why? We get stuck in our comfort zone, or we become so used to depending on certain people that it becomes overwhelming to think about breaking free.

We may even ignore the signs that it's time to grow. Or, even more simply put, we are afraid to take the risk and fail. As we get older, the consequences of certain choices are easier to understand: you could get hurt or lose a friend. I get it. But it is a critical element of growth. If you want to challenge yourself mentally, you need a friend who will ask the tough questions. If you are ready to grow physically, you need a friend who will remind you to make healthier choices or force you to go running. And when you embrace a stronger spiritual "self," you will benefit from those around you who can remind you of your faith. This doesn't mean you need to cut people out of your life or stop being friends with somebody; I'm just reminding you to always be on the lookout for ways you can continue to grow.

That Winners Travel dinner inspired me. I told the girls *my* dreams too. I told them that I wanted to write a book and become a motivational speaker. I wanted to tell the story of Winners Travel to the world. I just hadn't yet been able to get it off the ground. That dinner did it for me. When I saw their faces as we identified their goals and next steps, and then realized their lives had forever changed right before my eyes, I knew I had to get started. I knew that for the rest of my life, I wanted to help people live the Winners Travel way. I continue to view that dinner as a miracle.

I recently had an opportunity to hang out with Jim Clements, the president of Clemson University. He's now on my Top Five list. He balances a family life with a demanding job—something I will admit that I sometimes struggle with. I know that I need somebody like Jim to help me become even better in this area. I've already grown after just a couple of meetings with him.

Remember that as your life changes, your Top Five can change too. I challenged the girls that night to continually update their Top Five, and now I'm challenging you to do the same. Make a list of your current Top Five and a list of who you want to be in your Top Five. Then go out there, and find them!

# CHAPTER 6

# Look for the Miracles

*"All things are possible for the one who believes."*
— Mark 9:23

O NE NIGHT, A TEENAGER WALKED into the emergency
room where I was working my shift. He was thin—about
seventeen years old—and he was coughing and wheezing.

"I was mowing the grass, and I think I'm allergic to it!"
he wheezed. "I think I'm having an allergic reaction. I need
help, Doc."

"Yessir, young man, I gotcha," I replied. "When did this start?"

Little did I know what was about to happen to us.

I was now officially a family doctor and, man, was I ready
to start my career! Kelliegh and I had just completed residency

in Charlotte, North Carolina, and we made the decision to move back to Sumter, South Carolina—our hometown. I know what you're thinking: *Clay, Winners Travel . . . you're just going back home? Huh?*

The truth is, Kelliegh and I just missed our hometown. We did make an effort to look for the next place for us everywhere we went, but we just didn't find anywhere better than home. Plus, our goals of owning our own farm and giving back to the people living in the town where we grew up drove us to finally realize that there really is no place like home. I was in the middle of opening up a Lowder family practice but was still three months away from the actual opening. In the meantime, Tuomey Hospital, which was helping me start my practice, directed me to work their emergency room shifts. I was a young gun, and I thought I could handle it.

That particular night, we were slammed. Every bed was full, and everyone was scrambling; we were just trying to get through the night.

When Ricky came in, he looked fine to me. All his vital signs were good. He was coughing and wheezing, but not in distress. He was a good-looking fellow with short black hair and soft, innocent brown eyes. As he looked at me, I could see his eyes begging me to fix whatever was happening to him.

A young, hotshot respiratory therapist opened the curtain and peeked in on us.

"Hey, Doc," he said, "do you want me to give him a double?"

"Oh, that would be great!" I replied.

A "double" meant that he was going to give Ricky two doses of a breathing treatment that usually aborts an asthma attack.

I was thankful for the help as I was already way behind. The radio sounded again. There was an accident and more trauma patients were being brought in via ambulance. We groaned; we just weren't able to catch a break.

I left Ricky and the therapist, and went into high gear as I cleared some rooms out. The trauma patients arrived, and it took a while, but we finally got them all stabilized.

Then I walked by Ricky's room and decided to pull back the curtain to see how he was doing. But what I saw was not what I was expecting.

"Help!" I screamed immediately. *"Help!"*

Ricky was gasping for air. He was clutching his chest, and his eyes were wild with fear. He grabbed me and pulled me toward him. We both panicked.

He was in trouble. Every breath was forced and ended with a long coughing spasm. He was writhing all over that room.

*"HELP!"* I screamed louder. *"I need help now!"*

Finally, some nurses arrived. We all grabbed Ricky.

"OK, buddy, let's lie down here." I pleaded.

We tried to coax him down, but he was having none of it.

He went crazy and started fighting all of us. He may have been thin, but he was as strong as an ox. It took six of us to get him down.

A quick glance of his monitors told me everything I needed to know. His heart rate was over two hundred (a normal rate is sixty to one hundred beats per minute), and his breathing was fifty times a minute versus the normal twenty. His oxygen levels were dipping by the second, and he was starting to turn a deep shade of blue. He tried to sit up with every breath.

Everyone looked at me. I knew I appeared flustered and I was; I couldn't even catch my own breath.

*OK, Clay, get it together,* I told myself.

My training took over at that point, and I took a deep breath. I knew what to do. First, I called a code: a call for all hands on deck—for the best nurses, respiratory therapists, and aids to come with monitors, crash carts, etc. I ordered Versed, which is an amazing sedative that works instantly. A large nurse was able to hold Ricky's arm down long enough to stick an IV in and let the Versed pulse through his body.

Finally, Ricky let go. He chilled out and his head fell back against the pillow.

"You're OK, buddy. Just relax; we got you," I said.

We gave him a little more Versed to keep him calm.

Next, I had to take care of the severe wheezing. With Ricky relaxed, I was able to slide an endotracheal tube down his throat, and I hooked it up to a ventilator.

"Thank God!" I sighed. "That was close."

The ventilator is a pretty powerful machine that forces air into the lungs. You can control the settings, so I dialed the machine up to 100 percent oxygen and waited.

The monitors blinked. I looked again, but his oxygen level was dropping even further than before! I made more adjustments. Still, his breathing grew worse and became more erratic. He was becoming combative again and almost pulled the tube out himself.

*What in the world?* I asked myself. *This always works!*

Ricky's lungs were so tight that even the jet stream of oxygen from the ventilator could not get in. He was in deep trouble.

My instincts took over. I got loud, but I was firm with my commands and remained in control.

"Call Richland Hospital. I need the pediatric intensive-care doctor on call."

The doctor walked me through every treatment possible, even some experimental ones. Sadly, I had tried them all.

After quite a long conversation, he said, "Clay, prepare yourself."

"Prepare myself? For what?"

"He may die."

I froze. My mind would not go there. I guess I knew deep down that a lot of people die from asthma attacks each year, but I wasn't ready to accept it happening on my watch. I demanded a helicopter.

"Now!" I shouted to the staff.

Unfortunately, the weather was terrible, so it would be an hour before the helicopter would arrive. I swallowed the lump in my throat.

"Get his family in the meeting room, please," I asked the aid. My voice shook this time, and I found that I was no longer in control of myself. I honestly couldn't believe this was happening, and I wasn't prepared to face a patient's death this soon into the official start of my career.

After taking a deep breath, I pulled myself together and entered the family room. A little African-American lady, approximately seventy years old, was sitting there patiently.

"Hey, Doctor. How is Ricky?" she asked me.

I could not hide the look on my face.

"Well," I started slowly, "he's a sick fella."

I had received extensive grief counseling training, and so I switched gears from doctor to counselor. The main thing I knew I needed to do was recap the events and build up to the ending.

"He, umm, he . . . well, he came in with some wheezing after mowing grass earlier today. We thought it was an asthma attack, so we gave him some meds, and we have been watching him closely."

I looked away after I said that part, but I carried on, slowly and deliberately. I walked her through every moment. She had leaned in and was hanging on every word.

I finally got to the point.

"Sorry, he may very well . . . die," I spit out, choking up.

When I got to the word *die,* she grabbed my hand, put it in hers, and squeezed it—hard. I will never forget that squeeze. It shocked me.

"Son, I'm praying for you."

She stared directly into my eyes, and didn't break her focus. I started to speak, but she cut me off again.

"I am praying for you."

I looked away.

"I'm sorry," I stammered. "I'm a believer too, but he's really sick, and I just don't think he is going to make it." I was firm that time.

She squeezed my hand harder.

"Go back in there. Go back to my grandson now. He'll be OK; I talked with God! Go!"

She shooed me out with a wave of her hand, indicating I had no choice but to go back to the room where Ricky was.

I was a little perplexed; maybe my grief training wasn't the greatest. She did not seem to be prepared for what was happening. But I hustled back to Ricky. All the nurses were huddled around my boy, praying. The head nurse, a real go-getter, looked at me and frowned. A quick glance at the monitors showed he was worse than before. We all understood the signs: he was not going to live. The ventilator kept jamming, and his heart was starting to skip. I put my hands on his chest, and we all prayed for one minute straight.

Then it happened. The miracle. All of a sudden, the ventilator started singing!

*What the . . . ?* I thought to myself. I was amazed.

The air was going through his lungs now. It was awesome. It did not take but a minute until his numbers reversed and his heart rate started to settle. His oxygen hovered around 90 percent.

We all smiled, and there were sighs of relief heard throughout the room as we watched the color return to his cheeks. He was totally calm now. What an ordeal; what a turn of events!

Minutes later, the helicopter team flew through the door. A thick alpha male led the way. They were jacked up and ready for battle.

He slung the curtain back and stared at the boy.

"He's . . . he's fine. His vitals are all normal!" he exclaimed, glaring at me.

"I know, sir. I know," I grinned.

I almost skipped back to the family room, thrilled to deliver the news to Ricky's grandmother, but to my shock, no one was there. I looked all over. She was gone. I sat down in the same chair and choked up again. This was the first time I had sat down all night due to the patients cycling in and out.

I was still fairly shaken up when I got home, so I woke up my wife. I had to tell someone what had happened. She got me a Coors Light out of the fridge in an attempt to calm me down. I practically chugged it. Kelliegh just sat there and listened; she was stunned by it all. She held me tight. I realized that the event with Ricky had shaken me to my core; I was so focused when I was trying to save him that I hadn't let my mind wander beyond what needed to be done right there in the moment. The truth is, that boy almost died. It hit me all at once while I was sitting with my wife in the kitchen, and chills ran up and down my body.

I have told that story hundreds of times since then, and my voice cracks every time. I can feel my eyes well up, and my face still gets hot from nervousness. If I close my eyes when I tell the story, and let myself go back to that night, I can feel his grandmother's hand grab mine. It's still a part of me, but I am so thankful that I saw it. It seems that the Lord had me there for a reason that night, and I believe that I'm supposed to tell people about it. When I do, the story really catches people's attention. They lean in, listen intently, and are usually just as amazed as I was.

So why is this story important? It's about faith. Among the other things I talk about, Winners Travel is also about miracles. It's about perspective and seeing the world in a different way. Sometimes you just have to trust that you are in the right place at the right time, and there is a good reason for it. You may not realize it for years, but if you believe it, you will see it. I know that it sounds cliché or cheesy, but I really believe it's true. As I've said in earlier chapters, there are signs all around us. They may not all be obvious, but they are there, guiding us through the decisions we do (or do not) make.

I have always believed in miracles, and I have seen a lot of them throughout my life. Working in the medical field exposes me to

> Winners Travel is about miracles and seeing the world in a different way. Sometimes you just have to trust that you are in the right place at the right time.

many of them. Often, people attribute miracles to the development of modern technology, but I am here to tell you that technology is not everything. I began to record these miracles, and plan to discuss them in another book in the near future.

I view everything that I've learned about the human body as a miracle. It is a difficult thing to grasp that we just evolved into these intricate organisms out of nowhere. No, I believe that we are divinely created. There is no shortage of medical stories that medical science cannot explain, and I love it when that happens. I believe a Winners Travel life is filled with wonder about these miracles, and part of Winners Travel is to understand ty. I urge you to read about the miracles that can not be explained. Study them. They will really make you think.

My friend and preacher, Perry Noble, seems to experience things each week that he can incorporate into his sermons. When I asked him how he always seems to have a story, he replied, "Clay, I'm looking for stories. I'm expecting them."

In the same way, I think we, too, should be looking for miracles in our lives. We should be expecting them. They don't have to be major life-saving, earth-shattering miracles like Ricky; they can be simple and sweet. Why is it so important to look for miracles around us? Well, I think it changes our brain. It makes us thankful. It puts us in our place. It reduces anxiety and calms our soul. Winners Travel is about all that. We need to use our minds to relax our bodies. In today's crazy world, our minds usually do the opposite. From our phones to our computers to our smart-speaker systems, we are surrounded by buzzing, chirping, whirring, beeping, and dinging. It's easy to get distracted and spiral deep into a world of time-wasting videos and forget to look around ourselves. I mean *really* look around. When was the last time you stepped outside without a phone and looked

> Looking for miracles around us forces us to be thankful. It puts us in our place. It reduces anxiety and calms our soul.

up at the clouds in the sky? Observing miracles large and small makes us healthier, mentally and spiritually. If both of these areas are in good health, I believe our bodies begin to relax and heal themselves in some way.

I'll illustrate an example with a story. While I was working on this book, I had a man come in to my office for his follow-up visit for his frequent headaches. On his last visit I'd given him some migraine meds, but we also spent time talking about his depression and lack of sleep. I thought the two might be related, so I talked about the importance of spiritual health and I gave him a copy of *The Noticer* by Andy Andrews. It's a book about miracles and perspective. When he came back to the office for his follow-up, he was excited. He said his headaches were gone. In fact, he had never even taken any of the meds I'd prescribed during his prior visit. He said he'd started reading and thinking. This led to better sleep, which began the healing process in his body. Because he'd decided to open his mind to the idea of miracles, he was able to reset his thoughts on healing, and he suddenly started to feel better. His story isn't the only one out there; I've seen this happen again and again.

It can happen for you as well. If you want to be healthy, you have to learn to turn your mind off and relax your brain. I try to do it daily because my brain typically runs a million miles an hour. Read my morning routine on the next page and adopt the parts that work for you when you wake up in the morning.

- Have a seat in your favorite chair with a hot cup of coffee (if you like it).

- Sit up, nice and tall, and take a deep breath.

- Just breathe and listen.

- Make a list in your head of the top three things that you are thankful for.

- Dwell on them briefly—or you can say them as a prayer, if you'd like.

When I go through my routine, I usually look at the pond outside my window, and just go where my mind takes me. I say, "Today, Lord, Thank you so much for _____." I don't have any preconceived thoughts; I just go where I'm led. Often, it's to deep thoughts about my kids or Kelliegh, but sometimes it's much simpler, like just noticing the reflection in my pond.

Once I started being thankful for that reflection, I began to notice it every time I passed the pond. I see the trees and grass through it in a whole new way. It opened my mind. It's hard to stay stressed when I am staring at the calm, peaceful beauty of that pond. And, after a minute or so of contemplation or prayer, I'm done. Short and sweet wins. Doing this allows me to start my day on a healthy, expectant note. The world slows down.

After you perform this routine a few times, you will start to catch yourself thinking about the things you listed that morning as you go about your day. Your senses will become alive. Enjoy them. Think about them. We can see so clearly, smell the flowers, and hear things like tree leaves rustling in the wind or waves crashing in the ocean. Speaking of the ocean, I am picturing it now: *How does it work? How vast is it? What a miracle that ocean is!*

Remember, the miracles you take notice of can be small or large.

Beating cancer and surviving a major car wreck are examples of large miracles that are obvious, but small miracles are around us every day. Taking a breath, seeing your child smile, or even noticing the trees and sky can be the small miracles you notice. We always think that in order to believe in a miracle, we need something major to happen, but we forget to notice the little details.

Practicing the art of gratitude will change your life. It will make you smile and put a skip in your step. It doesn't happen overnight, and you will have to train yourself to get into the routine, but you can do it. Once you have a grateful heart, your eyes will open to the miracles around you. You will expect them.

I sure am thankful that I was at the hospital when Ricky cut his grass that day. The stress was incredible, but the dancing and celebration in that ER afterward was worth it. I will never forget it. Thank you, Lord.

One of my favorite sayings sits on a board on a wall in my house. It sums up the way Winners go about their days:

Work like you do not need the money.

Love like you've never been hurt.

Dance like nobody's watching.

I'll add another line myself: Look for the miracles!

# CHAPTER 7

# The Future of Medicine

*"Your future is whatever you make it.*
*So make it a good one!"*
— Doc Brown in *Back to the Future*

ROBERT CRUMP IS MY BUDDY. He's been a patient of mine since I started my practice. He is paraplegic, meaning that he is paralyzed from the waist down. I will tell you, though, Robert always practices gratitude. He thanks the nurses who help him, and he always flashes a big grin at me. I never leave the room without receiving a compliment from him. He sees a lot of doctors, but he makes me feel special. He said to me the other day, "You listen to me and you think, Clay. Dr. So-and-So doesn't." I recently discovered Robert has lymphoma, but he is still all smiles and maintains a grateful attitude. He motivates me to be a better person.

In return, I like to give hope to Robert. A couple of years ago, I saw that a paraplegic kicked a soccer ball to start off the World Cup games. Not only did he kick it, he walked up to it and booted it under his own brain's power. He felt it. I did some research and found out that he had a robotic suit on, which used a hat to capture his brain waves. It sent a signal to his legs, and then a hydraulic network moved them.

The guy had been confined to a wheelchair since 2006. Since then, Robert and I talk about it all the time. What a miracle that was! Now, when I want to lift Robert's spirits, I say, "Hey, Robert, the robots are coming!" He knows exactly what I mean.

And that's just the tip of the iceberg. Yessir, the robots are here! But not in the way you might think. They are here to help us. The future of medicine is bright in this area. The technology that is starting to emerge is mind-blowing and will help millions of people.

Medicine will likely change more in the next twenty years than in the past two thousand combined. Winners need to know about these advances. We need to stay on top of them to help ourselves and our loved ones get the best treatment. Understanding these advances will also provide us with hope. Hope is one of the most important emotions necessary for the body to heal mentally, physically, and spiritually. You don't need to be a doctor to give out hope. If someone you love has an illness, study it. Read all about it. You'll likely find a seed or two of hope layered in your research there somewhere. You can then tell your loved one what you read about or share a treatment for his or her condition.

> **Hope is one of the most important emotions necessary for the body to heal mentally, physically, and spiritually, and you don't need to be a doctor to give out hope.**

This is why I and other doctors went into medicine. I wanted to create novel solutions and be able to give hope to my patients. I wanted to help cure conditions. If I get stumped on a problem, I go straight to the books, and I study the latest therapies. I keep a subscription to UpToDate, a medical site that reviews all the diagnostic and therapeutic solutions available. It includes treatments like acupuncture, herbal medicine, and even CBD oil. I read through UpToDate often to keep my mind open to alternative treatments that can help my patients. Seeing the number of new studies and healing solutions out there gives me hope, and I am able to pass it along.

Now, some days, I just feel like I am reacting to problems. I am fighting with insurance companies just to get the best drug covered. I am a patient advocate, and go to battle for my patients until they get what they deserve. I will keep doing it, but it is frustrating to get turned down for doing the right thing over and over again; that's what burns all these doctors out. I cannot wait for the day when doctors are free from fighting insurance companies. We need to move on to bigger solutions, like developing a robot suit for people who need it.

There is one medical device out there that I feel will provide significant change. Can you guess what it is? Maybe a scanner or a machine that changes our thoughts? (No, I wish.)

Nope! In fact, I think you probably already have one. In fact, it's probably in your pocket right now. That's right—your smartphone! The smartphone will start the medical revolution. It will help patients more than we can imagine.

How? First, it provides instant access to information. With it, we can gain knowledge rapidly and reliably all over the world. There are sick people in Sumter, but this will especially help people in third-world countries.

A few years ago, I went to rural Romania with my brother-in-law, Tripp Waynick. We met Pastor Cornel Fedor there. Cornel is a traveling preacher who serves remote—and I mean *remote*—villages. He is a Winners Travel guy. He has dedicated his life to visiting those villages. He takes care of the widows, and needless to say, he is selfless. I wanted to be more like him.

So I teamed up with Cornel's efforts and organized a team of medical professionals, including my family, to set up rural health clinics in these villages. The first day, we went to a village near the city of Gherla in Romania. When Cornel steered us around the last turn in his 1990s Volkswagen van, I saw the schoolhouse in which we were going to set up, and I gasped. There were people lined up for three blocks. They waved frantically at us as we drove by. I looked into their eyes and saw hope. Most of them had bright crystal-blue eyes that sparkled in the sun. I could tell that they had been dreaming about this moment; they were hoping to receive the care and help they needed. You want to talk about Winners Travel? Most of them had walked for more than two hours to get to the school, and it wasn't over flat land either.

I was most humbled. They even made a sign for me. If you want to see both the sign and their faces, please go to the following website and click on "Romania": www.claylowder.com.

After we settled in to our clinic and opened the doors, patients started pouring inside. One man with a growth on his left cheek sat down in the chair in front of me. It was red and ulcerated, and it stuck out like a horn.

Through the interpreter, I asked, "How long has that been there?"

He replied that there was no time to talk about it. He was in urgent need of his blood pressure meds, as he had run out of them three months prior. He had no money and could not afford the trip to Cluj-Napoca, one of the more populous cities, to see the doctor and get medicine, much less to have surgery.

"Well, that has got to come off! You need to go to the hospital!" I told him.

"No way!" he replied.

He was stubborn, he was broke, and he was not going to the hospital. He looked deep into my eyes and begged me to do it right there in the clinic.

"I'll try," I said, "but it is risky because of where it is."

I did not need my "informed consent" papers signed. He and I both knew and accepted the risks. It was squamous cell cancer, and it needed to come off. I have removed hundreds of them, but this one was close to the temporal artery, and I did not want to accidentally nick it.

Tripp held up the light from his phone, and I began. It all went smoothly until the very last cut.

I looked up at Tripp and said, "Let's pray first."

We paused and prayed. I took a deep breath.

"Here we go," I said as I made the final cut.

The blade smoothly sliced off the "horn."

I had my suture needle ready, but there was no bleeding. We all let out a sigh.

The man was grateful. He wanted to give me his prized chicken as a payment, but what would I do with it? To this day, he often has Cornel send me pictures of my handiwork, and it looks great. I just love my job!

When I think back on it, I realize how great it would have been to have had my ENT buddy (who specializes in conditions from the neck up) on FaceTime, walking me through the surgery. There were many minor conditions on which I could have used a consult. This is why I look forward to seeing technology continue to develop. I cannot wait to help people through a smartphone in the future.

In fact, I believe that Apple will become a medical company. I hope it clears my waiting room out. My patients hate that waiting room, and so do I! Someone once said to me, "Well, if I wasn't sick when I got here, then I might be now!"

I predict that 90 percent of medicine will eventually be done through remote monitoring. FaceTime and livestreaming will improve so much with the new 5G that we will use it to visit with patients. Even now, most visits do not need to take place at my office, especially if they are routine follow-ups. I think that will become the case more often as technology continues to improve.

The new smartwatches have begun helping as well, but I believe they will continue to revolutionize medicine. They already monitor heart rates and rhythms well, but, hopefully, accurate blood pressure readings will also be accessible in the future through smartwatches. Blood pressure is a major silent killer, and I believe it is skyrocketing in most people, and they don't even know it. People refuse treatment every day. They blame their high blood pressure reading on "white coat syndrome"—a phenomenon in which patients in a clinical setting register a blood pressure level that is higher than normal—or they simply claim to have been upset when they arrived at the office. Maybe this is so, but a watch will prove it is not just a fluke. Blood pressure is directly attached to stroke and heart attack. It is now being implicated in memory loss and Alzheimer's disease. New data says the top number should be under 120. I have to have constant monitoring and patient buy-in to get it there. The watch would do both. In fact, a watch would have changed my dad's life. He has had to check his blood sugar five to six times a day for the past fifty-five years.

Last year, I diagnosed a six-year-old boy, Bryce Hanson, with diabetes. He is a brittle Type 1 diabetic. He is now checking his blood sugar seven times a day, even during the night. How frustrating it must be for him and his family. His parents, John and Kristall, are wonderful and relentless, but they're constantly exhausted. They love their son enough to check it fifty times a day if they needed to, but it would help this family immensely if his blood sugar readings and insulin pump were linked to his phone or watch. I tell Bryce about this theory of mine all the time and remind him, "It won't be long, buddy."

Here's a short side story: Bryce's sugar plummeted at a softball game, but I was on it. As I held Bryce and the orange juice I was trying to get him to drink, a crowd gathered. I felt an arm around me. A small hand squeezed my shoulder. I looked up to see Connor, Bryce's brother, hugging me.

"Thanks for taking care of my family, Dr. Clay," he said with tears in his eyes.

I melted.

Did I mention that I love my job?

So, back to my thoughts on technology. In the past, illness would even prevent travel. Certain illnesses kept people at home because they had to be close to their doctor or hospital. Now, with remote monitoring, there's more opportunities for those people to see the world. Hopes and dreams will return to those with an itch to see the world but have not been able do so as a result of illness.

One of the biggest advances in technology will be in understanding genetics. I leaned genetics in medical school, but I now see that some of what I was taught was just wrong. In fact, it's been said that 50 percent of what I was taught in medical school was wrong. (I wish I knew which fifty percent that was!)

Here's a story to illustrate genetics and disease: I just put my wife's uncle, Scott Kinder, in the hospital. He is fifty-three and fit as a fiddle. He is even training for a marathon. He had some chest pain and thought it was reflux. I checked him out anyway. The stress test looked normal; however, I thought it could be abnormal due to a small shadow shown on the test. I sent him to a cardiologist.

"I don't think this is cardiac. I think we can wait," the cardiologist said.

"Hey, man, this is my family. Could you please do a cath on him today?" I asked.

"I will," he agreed reluctantly.

He called me back an hour later.

"Are you sitting down, Clay?" He sounded serious.

I assured him I was sitting, and he continued: "Mr. Kinder has severe heart disease. He needs bypass surgery as soon as possible. If he had gone for a run tomorrow, he would have been gone."

Immediately, I called Scott and Cristi. I had chills running up and down my spine; I couldn't believe it. What if I hadn't pushed for the cath? What if I hadn't even checked him out to begin with?

His family was shocked but very grateful. They had just lost their young daughter Lexie the year before and felt blessed to have avoided another catastrophe.

But isn't that unexpected? A fifty-three-year-old with zero risk factors who has severe heart disease. His family wanted to know how this could have happened, and my only answer was that it had to be genetic.

In fact, most diseases are. There was a discovery made in 2003 that will change all of our lives. They cracked our genome. It turns out, we are not as complicated as we had thought. We have only around twenty-six thousand genes. That is about what an ear of corn has!

With this knowledge, we will be able to develop more and more specialized cures for specific illnesses. The first of these treatments is under study already, with gene therapy. Hopefully, it will allow us to rid the world of Parkinson's and Alzheimer's. I am not sure how you feel about it, but I have seen suffering in my family from both of these conditions, so we have been happy to follow the news about gene therapy. You might be surprised by what you learn to accept and become open-minded about when your own family is going through something. You'll accept practically anything if it means the pain and suffering of your family will go away.

Meachelle Clea is one of my favorite patients. I saw her as a teenager over twenty years ago, and now she is a mother of three. She has sickle cell anemia and it plagues her. The crises come often and require hospital admissions for pain control. But, no matter how bad she is hurting, she smiles and laughs at my terrible jokes. She and I have a close bond. I think it all started when I found that an infected toe was to blame for her very first crisis.

I give Meachelle hope. I tell her of the future. I coach her.

"Meachelle, you have a mutation. You're a mutant!" I joke with her. "Soon, I'll be able to fix you. We will have the technology to rebuild you." (Anyone else remember *The Six Million Dollar Man* TV show?)

> The medical future is promising. I think we will be able to plug symptoms into a computer, and let it help us—with artificial intelligence—to diagnose.

Gene therapy is on its way. I keep telling Meachelle that when the day finally comes, I am signing her up!

The future is promising. I also hope we move to new ways to diagnose. I think we will be able to plug symptoms into a computer, and let it help us—with artificial intelligence—to diagnose. I am here to help people, but I need help too! Doctor's aren't perfect, and sometimes there are issues that require a few different tests and solution options. If we had artificial intelligence to sift through the data and help us diagnose or even check up on patients, the door to a doctor's office may open even further. They'll have more time and the patients will thank them for it.

I also predict that soon you will be able to go to your family doctor and get your cheeks swabbed, and your DNA will reveal your risks for common diseases. Is it far better than getting your blood drawn? In a way, yes—these swabs will direct the specific care needed.

My dad is a good example of this. He had minimal risks for the number one killer, heart disease. I used a stress test and echocardiogram to evaluate him. His tests were abnormal, and I found he had a 95 percent widow-maker blockage on a heart catheterization. This discovery saved his life. Some people though, are not so lucky; sometimes the stress test misses a problem. Remember, it is a grey science, and sometimes people even refuse the test.

"It is invasive, I don't want that!"

They say this all day to me.

So what if I could easily perform a DNA test? I think more people would do it, and it would save lives.

When you save someone's life, it's a pinnacle moment, especially if it's your dad or your uncle. It really gives me hope. It is what drives me to press on and what has inspired me to write *Winners Travel.* I want people to know what's out there. Being equipped with knowledge in this age of developing technology is vital. To have holistic health, you have to be armed with it. Go to your family doctor yearly. Listen to them, and do what they say. It will likely save your life too.

So how exactly would a genetic swab help you? Let's say your swab shows you have the heart-blockage gene. If it is positive, we can skip the additional testing (stress test and echocardiogram, for example), and go straight to heart caths. If you're in your twenties, we can also perform advanced cholesterol tests and prevent the heart arteries from building plaque in the first place.

I consider myself a preventer. That fits into my style of practice.

On another note, colon cancer is common and preventable. However, the national recommended age to start screening is fifty. Testing that late in patients' lives can cause a lot of misses. In fact, I have had two friends die in their forties of colon cancer. What a travesty. When we eventually have DNA testing for colon cancer, we can test people easily when they are in their twenties. If positive, those individuals can get colonoscopies every five years. Even one life saved is worth it to me.

The future of medicine is bright. Yes, it is aggravating and time consuming to go to your doctor now, but trust me, we are working on it. In the meantime, you must take action now to make your health a priority. Protect yourself by staying up to date with the latest and greatest technology. Get a yearly physical because early detection is the key.

I guess you could say, "Winners Travel to the doctor." Include your physical health in your goals this year. Get a plan and take action today.

One of my favorite doctors is Dr. Emmett Brown. Yes, the one from *Back to the Future*—the "Great Scott!" guy. He created the "flux capacitor" that makes the time machine, a

DeLorean car, go back in time. I know it's just a movie, but his character was just brilliant. At the end of the film, Marty McFly, the main character, asks "Doc" about the future. Doc says, "Your future hasn't been written yet. No one's has! Your future is whatever you make it. So make it a good one!"

I love that, and I smile every time I hear it. As a doctor, I have to believe in the future, and I have to provide hope. If you believe that the best is yet to come, you will understand what I'm saying. Repeat Doc's statement, and pray for the future to continue to develop. Study it, please, and tell it to other people. I do. I tell my paraplegics, diabetics, and even Alzheimer's patients that.

Don't stop believing!

CHAPTER 8

# Laugh Out Loud

*"A merry heart doeth good like a medicine."*
— Proverbs 17:22

A PATIENT OF MINE, MICHAEL, IS autistic, and he sees me often. He is a huge Pittsburg Steelers fan and wears black, oversized warm-up pants and a black-and-yellow Steelers jacket to my office every time he visits. Oh, and he also has a flat-bill Steelers hat that he wears tilted to the left.

Michael's dad, used to bring him in to his appointments. I took care of him too. He was much older than Michael and was in poor health. His father was Italian, and I was mesmerized by his accent. He would wave his fingers to add emphasis to each carefully chosen word.

"Doctor Lowder, you are a good man. Will you take care of Michael as his doctor when I am not here?"

"Yes, sir," I replied. "Please don't worry. I'll be here for him! I'll make sure he's all right."

Michael's father sighed. "Come here; come here," he motioned with his fingers. He gave me a giant, warm Italian hug. His eyes were moist.

"Thank you, Doctor," he said, choking up.

After his father passed away, I was able to get Michael placed in a local community home. They watch him closely there, and I insist they bring him to my office often. There is one visit I will never forget.

"Michael, how ya doin', brother?" I asked in my best broken Southern-Italian drawl.

"My side hurts," he replied with zero emotion on his face.

"Where?"

"Right side. My side hurts."

"Exactly where, Mike?"

"Right side. My side hurts."

We were not getting anywhere. I ran a few tests. The blood work and a gallbladder ultrasound were normal. I did not know what else to do.

"Why don't you x-ray me?"

I shrugged, "Why not? But, Michael, x-rays usually don't show much on your belly."

I was wrong. There was a sharp, two-inch sewing needle buried in his right side. No wonder he was in pain!

"Michael, you have a needle in there! How did it get there?" I asked.

"I have no idea! My side hurts."

"OK, buddy, I need to do a little surgery, and I'll try to get it out."

"My side hurts."

You get the picture. So I numbed up his skin, which made him a little confused.

"What are you doing?" he asked over and over. He was restless.

"Almost got it," I said.

I learned that from Kelliegh's grandfather, Kelly, long ago. It is a trick he used to get people to relax. One day, Kelliegh's brother Brent got a fishing hook stuck in his foot. He was combative, and we couldn't hold his foot still long enough to get the hook out. But Kelliegh's grandfather shouted, "I got it!" and Brent, thinking the hook had actually been removed, relaxed for a second to see. Kelly jerked the hook out at that very moment. This trick works every time with patients of mine.

So I'm performing this surgery, and I still cannot quite find the needle. After thirty minutes, and a lot of digging around and repeating, "Almost got it," I scraped against metal. I teased one end open and that needle flew out of Michael's side. He sat straight up on the table.

"What was that?" he yelled.

"It's a sewing needle. How did it get there?"

"I have no idea. That's what I am asking you! My side hurts."

By that time, most of the medical assistants had heard the story. Everyone came to see the needle. We shared a big laugh and all wondered how it got there. The mystery has never been solved.

What a story! I have told it a hundred times. It reminds me of what I do not know and the healthy respect I should have for people and their different illnesses, but most of all, it makes me laugh. It makes me remember not to take it all so seriously.

I had a professor in medical school who did take things too seriously. He once gave me a C on a patient encounter, and I could not believe it. I stormed into his office. When I'm mad, I can't hide the emotion on my face, so he saw right away that I was ready to argue his decision.

"What happened, Doctor? That C is killing me!"

"Well, Mr. Lowder, you are too informal."

He played the VHS recording.

"Right here, you even laughed at your patient. You are a professional. Act that way. A little more formal is the way to go."

"Yessir, I will." I took a deep breath and turned and walked out.

As I left that room, my mind raced. I was not in any position to argue, but I definitely wanted to. My kids always say I was likely a "brownnoser," and I was. I liked getting good grades, so why ruffle the feathers of this guy? I was certain to keep a C if I did. But I knew he was wrong in his assessment.

Looking back on it after having run my practice for all these years, I can definitely say that he was wrong. He was an academic through and through—scholarly and intelligent, certainly, but to my knowledge, he had never practiced in the real world and didn't deal with patients everyday. I noticed that he had no bond with his patients. He did not even smile. I swore to myself that I would never be that guy.

While his critique of my patient encounter was for me to refrain from laughing, I actually did just the opposite; I learned to laugh *more*. But I always make sure that I do not laugh *at* my patients; I laugh *with* them. I tell them stories and joke around. I listen to *their* stories. I enjoy them and get to know them as a person first and a patient second. At that point, I have then earned the right to be their family doctor. The visits then go so much better, and they begin to tell me everything.

I also make it a point to use my first name. It's hard on most of them. When they say "Dr. Lowder," I look over my shoulder and insist, "It's Clay!"

My professor would hate that, but I don't care. He isn't issuing my grade anymore! My patients are, so I just want to make them feel happy, comfortable, and safe in their visits with me.

I like to ask different questions than most other doctors. By the end of the visit, I usually know their favorite college football team, and they know mine. (If Clemson ever loses, which is rare, they are sure to give me a hard time about it!) I like to know what they do for fun. I ask about their life dreams and goals. I have used tips on communication from my professors, but I have mainly learned these techniques for making conversation easy from farmers, preachers, teachers, and other mentors of mine far outside of the medical world. In fact, one of my favorite sayings comes from my fishing guide, Captain Tommy Scarborough.

"Lowder, you have got to be able to talk preacher with the preacher and drunk with the drunk!"

I love my South Carolina education. I smile and laugh when I think that most of it came from those with whom I grew up—not high and mighty professors.

In Proverbs, it says, "A merry heart doeth good like a medicine." I am sure to always practice that. When I open the door and go into that room, it's "showtime." I put on my best smile and make sure

> **A merry heart doeth good like a medicine.**

I laugh with as many patients as possible. My nurses and assistants are also encouraged to adopt this policy.

One of the best is Ashley Shirley, who became my medical assistant when she was nineteen. She had one special way to really "get" her patients. She would look a patient dead in the eye and tell them no, that she could not perform a certain request for them. She would let it hang for about ten to fifteen seconds before grinning and poking them with her elbow. "I'm just kidding!" she would exclaim, and then she'd double over laughing! We called her "LTL" for laughing too loud. We could always hear her in the next room. But boy, the patients loved her! They would often push me aside and say, "You get out of here, Doc. I'm here to see Ashley!"

On a side note, that attitude helped Ashley move up in the company to take on the role of chief operating officer for our office. We had a private equity group run our practice for a while, and I often say Ashley can run it far better than those boys from Brown or Wharton, partly due to her intelligence and hard work, but mainly due to her "merry heart." Ashley has the smarts to know what needs to happen, but the care and compassion to see everything through with love and tenderness for each of our patients.

Another great story about a "merry heart" is that of Pete. Pete is my good ol' buddy. He grew up in neighboring rural Lee County, and he fixes trucks. Unfortunately, Pete had no medical insurance.

He came to me one day with a major complaint: "I have a fish bone in my butt!"

"What in the world?" I asked.

"Well, you see, Doc, I was eating fried fish, like I know I shouldn't be, and somehow, I ate a bone and it got lodged coming out!"

"There is no way there's a fish bone back there," I said. "It's just impossible."

"I'll show you," Pete shouted as he jumped off the table and peeled his grease-covered coveralls down to his ankles. He bent over the table and sure enough, there was a bone sticking two inches out of his rear!

"How much?" he asked. "I ain't got no insurance."

I gasped and laughed.

"Well, Pete, I'll make a deal with you. If you let all my nurses come in while I remove it, it'll be free!"

"Deal, Doc!" he said.

I went into the hall.

"You aren't going to believe this," I said. "Come on, all of you."

We literally had ten people in there as I carefully extracted a fish bone from Pete's rear end! When it came out, I saw why it had become lodged there. It was in the perfect shape of a cross. Pete is a devout Christian, so that made him really proud!

"I told you it was a fish bone!" he said.

I still do not know how that bone traveled all the way through his intestines and almost made it out. Every time I see Pete now we share a big laugh.

"Eat any fish last night?" I always grin and ask.

To me, humor is part of the hope I keep talking about. It helps us heal and makes us better listeners as well. Always be on the lookout for a chance to laugh. Here's a challenge that will make you a better person. My duck-hunting partner and one of my best friends, Brandon Kinder, taught me this one. When you are having a conversation with someone, and they say something

> Humor is part of hope; it helps us heal and makes us better listeners as well.

that you find funny, even if just a little bit, immediately repeat what they said, and laugh out loud. At first, it will seem awkward, and you will even have to fake laugh sometimes, but you will become good at it. Here's the catch though: in order to do this, you have to listen *really* closely to what that person is saying. And that is what is endearing to people. It is a great habit and it makes people think that they are funny; plus, they feel attended to. Not *all* the things they say are funny, but don't let them know that.

My son Coker always picks on me. He will roll his eyes at me and say, "Dad, you're not *that* funny." Yet, when I'm with him, he listens carefully and laughs at a lot of the stupid stuff I say. When I'm with him, I feel funny. I'm at peace. He wants to be a psychologist, and he will be a good one because of this trait alone.

So will laughter help you mentally, physically, and spiritually? You bet! Laughter helps Winners Travel. But don't just take my word for it. I'll give you two additional references.

Think about the last time you had a sinus infection. If you are like most of my patients, you couldn't wait to get your Z-Pak. The next day you were better. Studies have shown that most "sinus infections" are viruses. But get this: Z-Paks don't affect viruses. However, everybody believes they need one, and they are emphatic that it made them better immediately. The power of belief is hard to beat. If you believe you will get better, then you *will* get better. The Bible says that a merry heart is just as good as medicine. I always remember that. When I open that exam room door, I put on my happy face no matter how stressed I might be. I smile and greet my patients. I don't shake hands anymore, as I feel it's got too much of a chance to spread infection to patients—or to me, for that matter. I do fist bumps instead. I call them "flu bumps." It took a little while for my older patients to catch on, but I think most appreciate it now. And I hug. I always say their name. I playfully tease them, and I do my best to provide some form of comic relief because I've found that it helps, especially for those patients who are waiting to hear about tough diagnoses or are worried about their health in general. They laugh with me. These seemingly small acts of connection get them to trust and believe in me. And they get better.

The second reference is my wife, Kelliegh. She has the best laugh; it's her greatest weapon. She can disarm anyone with it. For her and those around her, laughter *literally* is the best medicine. Her laugh is contagious. I've always said that since I made her laugh out loud the first time, I've spent the rest of life trying to make that happen again and again. She says, "Clay, you can't feel two emotions at the same time." She's right. I know laughing isn't an emotion, but happiness is, and laughter births happiness. It's simple: if you laugh, you can't be mad, right?

I have a gimmick that I employ when I do my motivational speaking. I ask the audience to stand up. Then I pull out my watch and ask that they laugh out loud for seven seconds. At first, I hear awkward and fake laughs. As everybody looks at each other and begins to realize they are all awkwardly laughing together, they start to *actually* laugh, and in no time, they grab their stomachs and laugh from their bellies. By the end of it, everybody in the audience is in hysterics. I then challenge them to start each day like that. Look into your mirror and belly laugh. Sure, it feels funny at first, and it will take some practice, but it will change you. It will help you heal and immediately start your day on a positive note. It will let your brain work the way God designed it to do. Who would have thought that you could learn to laugh? Well, you can. It will set you up for a happy, hopeful day. It will change you. It will make you stand out, and people will love you for it.

Winners Travel to laughter!

**LOL!**

CHAPTER 9

# Winners Travel

*"You become what you think about."*
— Earl Nightingale

IRECENTLY RECEIVED A FIVE-PAGE LETTER from a young man who used to be a patient of mine. He moved away from Sumter and is now managing his own business. I looked in his chart. I had only seen him twice in his late teenage years. I often get letters and cards from patients, but this one was special. I placed a thumbtack through it, and hung it on my board so that I could read it whenever I felt I was having a tough day.

His letter was heartfelt. In it, he explained how I'd seen him for a sore throat, but rather than prescribe him some medicine and quickly dismiss him from my office, I sat and asked him about his future. I used the line I use on most teenagers who come to my office: "Where do you see yourself in ten years?" He said it caught him off guard, but that he couldn't stop thinking about it. He said the prescription I gave him changed his life. It wasn't for a Z-Pak. I'd sent him out of the exam room with a brown paper towel, on which I'd scrawled the question above. I'd also written down two books for him to read.

Getting that letter was motivating, and I reflect on it often. It makes me want to ask everyone I see about their goals and dreams. As I hope you understand by now, Winners Travel is about helping others. Doing so is a big key to your happiness. It works. It makes you grateful and displaces your negative thoughts. Putting in the time and effort to care about somebody else's well-being—their mental, physical, and spiritual health—allows you to step away from selfish and self-serving thoughts. It opens up the opportunity to make unique and individual connections with those around you.

The second thing I reflect on from that letter is the impact that goal-setting has on young minds. I only saw that young man a couple of times, and yet I got a thank-you note years later that made my day and the days to come. You can get a letter like that too. I know I'm a doctor, so people regularly come to me for guidance, but I still have to be intentional every single day. I make the effort to sit with each and every patient and challenge myself to find a way to work the conversation so that I can ask about their dreams. If the patient is depressed, it's a little bit easier to get to their dreams because they are vulnerable and typically open to change. Most of the time, however, they are there for other reasons, like sinus infections or diabetes. In today's fast-paced medical practices, it's difficult to slow down and ask questions. Just because I have patients visiting me doesn't mean it's any easier to get these questions out; I could opt to be a machine, churning patients in and out as quickly as possible, prescribing this medicine and that medicine, just to get them out of my office so I can see the next person in the waiting room. When I get letters like the one from this young man, it reminds me how impactful one question can be. Make yourself ask questions. People want help. The more you do it, the easier it becomes to ask these questions of everyone you meet.

It takes a little practice in the beginning for some folks, so do what I did. Start with your family. Have a Winners Travel dinner with your family, and ask your kids this: "What is the secret to life?" There's no right answer, of course. After you enjoy your kids' answers, the next question to ask is, "Where do you see yourself in ten years?" You might get some vague responses at first. Prod on. "What does your house look like?" "What does your spouse look like?" "Where do you see yourself working?" Get specific too. "How

> "What is the secret to life?" There's no right answer, of course.

much money do you make?" "What kind of dog do you have?" "What's your dream vacation?" "How many kids do you want?" "What do they look like?" "What names do you like?"

The next step I take is called "The Compliment Game." This can easily become part of your Winners Travel dinners too. Coker, my son and my psychologist, invented it. He made us play the game together as a family in the car on the way to Disney World one day. It's easy. You take a piece of paper and write down all the positives you can think about somebody else in the room with you. Then you take turns reading them aloud in front of the group. Now, you'd better be ready and have some tissues handy. I think I cried half the way to Florida just from having heard what my kids thought about me. They loved the game too. Just think about how your kids will feel when you point out all of their positive attributes. In a world full of complaining and negativity, it's amazing to watch people receive compliments about themselves. They stick out their chests and walk taller. They seem to change instantly. Isn't that what we want most for our kids? The Compliment Game can ease tension in families. When we got to Florida, our whole extended family was there. After a few days of being bottled up in one house, some irritability was inevitable. Remember, the Lowders are fighters. Well, Coker Lowder stepped up.

He said, "I'm sick of this, we are playing The Compliment Game right now!"

Everyone groaned. He persisted, and after an hour, there was not a dry eye in the room. My brother Milt's little girls, McKee and Emerson, and Jim's daughter Ariail were really into it. They were between the ages of six and ten at the time, and I have to say, they stole the show. The compliments they gave were so deep. It taught me that you can't start The Compliment Game soon enough. And, it worked; the family relaxed and all the tension melted away. There were hugs everywhere. The love had returned.

You'll also be surprised by what people say about you, and what you come up with to say about them. At first, the compliments start off pretty superficial, as in, "You have the most beautiful curly hair," but as people warm up to the game, the compliments become very specific. You may not have even realized somebody thinks that about you. Someone may compliment you on the way you coolly and calmly answer the phone whenever somebody from work calls. You might not even be aware that this is something you do, but it sure does serve as an amazing boost of confidence!

After you have a Winners Travel dinner with your family and you are comfortable with how it works, move on, and ask a teenager you know to dinner. Maybe it will be easier for you to ask a teen group you know. A good place to start is with your kids' friends. Bring your son or daughter as well. They will amaze you with their answers, but remember that you may not get responses right away, and they won't be able to answer all of the questions nor will they feel comfortable doing so. That's OK; you are planting a seed that takes time to grow. I usually ask them to write the answers on a three-by-five-inch index card and bring it to me in four weeks, or whenever they feel ready to show me what they've written. If you are persistent and you nurture the growth, you'll get that seed to sprout. You might even help place somebody on the right path instead of the wrong one. It's gratifying. I believe that there is a bit of family doctor in everyone. It's not just about having a medical degree and knowing all the fancy terms for medicines, illnesses, and treatments; it's about connecting with real people and helping them to see their value by setting goals and milestones to hit along the way toward achieving those goals. This is your chance to try it out.

> **The Clay Lowder secret to life is all about making a game plan. Yes, you game plan your life!**

Here's what I've learned. It's the Clay Lowder secret to life! What is it? It's all about making a game plan. Yes, you game plan your life! Think about it: we create a game plan for everything else, so why not our lives? What must a ship captain do before taking a cruise ship out to sea and through the shallow waters of the Caribbean? That's right; he must map his course. He must have a game plan. What does a football coach do before the big game? He must work out a game plan.

How does it work?

Well, I believe it starts with a Winners Travel dinner; this is where you plant the seed. Then you take the ideas and write them down. Soon, I will teach you the exact way to do this. Once you have a map depicting where you are going, you can write out the baby steps you need to take to get there. Then you will have your game plan. Don't worry if you are older and feel that it's too late. There's nothing more irrelevant than the score at halftime; it's the final score that matters. In fact, former Clemson coach Danny Ford once said, "The most important part of the football game is the first five minutes of the third quarter." The teams he coached came out of the locker room ready to go in the third quarter. Are *you* ready to go? Is your team ready to go?

So how does it work? Well, it is sort of like brainwashing yourself. I have studied the brain. It is a miracle in and of itself, and it still isn't fully understood, but what we do know is that it can be programmed. That is right; it is a computer. Here is a quick and easy way to program your brain. Write your goals on your mirror with a dry-erase marker. (By the way, I didn't even know you could write on your mirror until my daughter, Liza, who was eight years old at the time, showed me how!)

A goal is just a wish unless you write it down. Writing it down actually focuses the brain on it like nothing else. Once it's written down, it becomes a real, tangible thing that the brain can work toward achieving. By writing and reading your goals, you begin to control your thoughts. You actually start to become them, and this can change your life. It seems that humans are conditioned to have negative thoughts. They come out of nowhere, and can come at any time. They whisper that you are no good and convince you that you will never be anything. I still get them, but have learned to control them. I have found that by reading my goals on my mirror aloud each day, I can quickly get rid of my negative thoughts. They are only fleeting thoughts now. So that's your game plan. You write your goals out, and you think about them. Then you *become* your goals. You become what you think about!

So, you might be asking me how I write out my goals. I work with a lot of people on goal-setting exercises. We address mental, physical, and spiritual goals together. I sometimes add in financial and family goals too. If you'd like to view a sample goal-setting exercise, please visit my website, www. claylowder.com.

Every New Year's Eve, I write out my goals for the upcoming year. I put my goals anywhere I know I will see them. I write them out on my mirror. I plug them into my phone and set a reminder on my calendar app, which pops up and makes me read through them daily. It takes my mind off all the small stuff that can bog me down each day.

I also created a goal board. Some people call this a "vision board." Last year, I sat down with my daughter and my wife, and we cut out pictures from magazines, representing what we want out of our lives, trips we want to go on, and things we want to see. We tried to include long-term goals too. I have placed a picture and explanation of my goal board on my website.

Goal-setting has always been a big part of my life. When Kelliegh and I were high school sweethearts and dreaming about having a house in the country with a farm and fishing ponds, we made our own version of the goal board mentioned above. We would draw our own pictures and cut out images from magazine articles. We never stopped visualizing what we wanted. We even took a trip across South Carolina to look at old plantation houses, and we took notes as we saw things we did (or did not) like. Kelliegh even went so far as to create a complete scrapbook of what she wanted. My wife is creative. When we went to buy our farm and build our house, the builder was amazed because Kelliegh already knew exactly what she wanted. Believe me, I didn't get in her way. We had dreamed and planned this since we were sixteen!

I've spoken at quite a few churches over the years, and I tell them the same game plan story. The ladies usually smile, nod, and say something like, "That's right; speak it! Speak it into existence." Exactly! They get it. The more you materialize your thoughts about your goals, the easier it becomes for you to stay on track to accomplish them. You may even find yourself subconsciously doing things that are helping to move you closer and closer to achieving your goals.

Over the years, I've also started to involve my friends in my goal-setting. I like to say my goals out loud to a third party, so I've shared my goals with most of my friends at some point along the way. They love being a part of this, and they challenge me to stay the course. Once somebody knows what you're trying to accomplish, they feel an obligation to help you see it through. Some of my goals are extensive, so sometimes I feel like I have to prove to my friends that I can achieve them. Once I verbally share my goals, it seals the deal; it makes me succeed.

One of my best friends is Jon Smoak. He will listen to me and give me his honest opinion of what he thinks when I share my goals. He has also adopted the Winners Travel philosophy with his own family—his wife, Lisa, and his beautiful daughters, Morgan and Hayley. I watched Lisa and Jon instill goal-setting into their girls' lives at an early age. Both girls are on their way now. Morgan works at a financial company full time, coaches volleyball on the weekends because it's her passion, and volunteers for a Down syndrome achievement center called GiGi's Playhouse as a way of giving back. Hayley just graduated from Clemson and is going to pharmacy school in the fall. Since she was ten years old, we have helped Hayley realize her goal to work in medicine. As teenagers are more likely to listen to an adult other than their parents, it's great for me to have friends like Jon and Lisa, who can motivate my own kids. I've seen both of them take my kids aside and whisper words of encouragement in their ears.

In fact, I've asked both of them to sit down and talk to our kids about their goals and any of the struggles they've had in achieving them.

We even have a Winners Travel group text, and I swear, it's better than a support group! The original members were the Lowders; the Smoaks; and Caddy Stukes, Clayton's girlfriend. Liza's boyfriend, Jake Meyers, and Hayley's boyfriend, Nick Gibbons, were recently asked to join our beloved WT group text. (We will see if they can stay in it.) The group text helps all of us focus on our goals and be accountable to ourselves and those we promised we would support—and we are getting better all the time. We have even now asked all of them to write their goals down.

Lisa, Jon, Kelliegh, and I write down a place we all want to go to together each year. Typically, Kelliegh and Lisa will pick a spot on the map, and John and I then plan it out. We've been to Boston, New York, Dallas, New Orleans, Phoenix, Miami, and San Francisco. We've also been all over the Caribbean. We even went to Turks and Caicos, where Jon and I learned to kiteboard. I think I'm still sore from that experience!

Traveling with good friends is a special thing. Our group travels all started out with a bet. Lisa is a huge San Antonio Spurs fan. One year, the Spurs were down three games in a best-of-seven series against the New Orleans Hornets.

I mouthed off, "No way the Spurs will win."

"Oh yes, they will!" Lisa snapped back. "You wanna bet?"

"Oh, yeah!" I said. This was easy money.

Lisa said, "OK, if the Hornets win, I'll give you a hundred bucks. But if the Spurs win, you have to take all four of us to San Antonio to watch them play the Lakers in the next series!"

I smirked.

"Game on."

I didn't watch one single game. A week later, Lisa burst into my office. She screamed at me a common Lowderism, "Let's Roll!"

"What happened?"

"The Spurs just won Game 7! When are we leaving?"

"What?"

My parents always taught me not to bet; however, I honored what we agreed upon. We got third-row seats and watched the Spurs beat the Lakers in San Antonio. It was the start of our Winners Travel trips together, and we always have at least one Winners Travel–focused dinner at each location. We continue to sharpen our minds and write down new goals and ideas for more trips we want to take together.

I ask my patients, too, to write down their trips and goals. I usually do not miss this opportunity with any teenager who comes to my office. Even if they are just in for a sore throat, I ask, "Where do you see yourself in ten years? What does life look like? What do your kids look like? How many do you have? How about your house, your boat, your car? Where is the coolest place on earth you'd like to see?" I ask them to write down their answers on an index card and bring it to me on their next visit.

They look at me funny, but a lot of them take me up on it. I will see them years later, and they will run up to me with their "goal card."

I have read several books by Earl Nightingale. He has a deep, husky radio voice, and my family and I love to listen to him. At one point, he said, "Out of one hundred men, only five succeed." He meant that at retirement age in the United States, very few men can retire well and not live off the government. I've set out to change that. How? We have to get young people to set up a game plan for their lives as soon as possible. *Now.* They have to dream, and we have to support them in their dreams. They need to have a Winners Travel game plan.

In addition to writing down long-term goals, creating travel plans, and dreaming big, setting small daily goals is just as important. Earl Nightingale was asked to consult with huge businesses in the hope he would try to change them. He talks about one technique of his that would revolutionize most of them. He would tell everyone at the company, "When you get here in the morning, take a sheet of paper and write down the top six things you need to do that day. Rank them in order of importance. Then, do not work on number two until you have completed number one."

It is simply amazing how well this works.

People always say to me, "Well it's easy for you to say and do; you're a doctor." Not true. This exercise will work for anybody in any profession. I've seen it play out. It forces you to really think about the most important tasks you need to get done that day: what do you need to do in order to feel more complete at work, or like you made progress in working toward your larger goal? Write it down and do exactly as I explained above; do not move on to number two until number one is complete. Don't work on number three until you have finished with number two, and so on.

I am a member of GHO, which stands for "Green Heads Only." Brandon Kinder, John Rivers, Bryan Caughman, and I are the board members. We go to Arkansas every year to shoot mallards in the timber. One day, something magical happened. We killed all greenheads during our hunt. For those that don't know, "greenhead" is the nickname for a male mallard. He has a head that's so green it even has a flash of blue in the bright sun. He is the prize duck. We usually have a few females or hens in our bag, but not that day. It was greenheads only! We were so thankful. We always pray together in the timber just before the hunt. That day, we prayed after the hunt too; we were giddy. We laughed like little kids throughout the whole trip. During the twelve-hour ride home, I told them the Winners Travel story. I told them about the goal-setting system. They loved it, and immediately adopted it for their families. You should see their lives now. They have all radically changed since then. Two of them are farmers and have added new crops, like string beans and hemp, to their farms. One member had a fantastic sales job, but he built another business from the ground up, and he now owns his own company. All three are well on their way to achieving all of their goals. They know how to "become what you think about," and they didn't have to go to medical school in order to be successful.

Green Heads Only now meets once a month but as a mastermind group. It is powerful. One of our plans is to mentor young men through the outdoor channel we know so well. It's nice to have dreams you can share with your family and friends. Find your "GHO" group today.

Now you're well on your way toward a Winners Travel mind-set. In order to see results, you have to have goals. For life to work, you have to have a game plan. Those written plans and ideas will control you and consume you. You will probably be too busy to think about your problems, but just remember that if negative thoughts start to creep in, take a deep breath and refocus on your goals. Say them aloud. Make yourself laugh.

In life, you will always be chasing dreams—traveling, always reaching for the next big thing, and improving your day-to-day life by achieving small goals, one at a time. Stay the course, and you will see amazing results. C. S. Lewis said, "You are never too old to dream a new dream or set a new goal." Maybe that is the secret to life.

What is your next step? What is your game plan? Dream it, and write it down now. Spell it out. It's the first five minutes of the third quarter.

# CHAPTER 10

# Winners Travel to Physical Health

*"We are all going to die; I've done the research!"*
— Clay Lowder "Lowderism"

**T**HE WEALTH FORMULA:

Your greatest wealth is health!

Take the number 1,000,000.

The number 1 is your health.

If you lose the 1, then all the 0s behind it don't matter!

Winners Travel is not possible unless you are healthy. Take action today!

\* \* \*

Bobby looked down when I entered the exam room. He tapped his watch and said, "Where have you been? I've been here almost an hour!"

With a straight face, I replied, "Oh, I went fishing this morning. Sorry I'm late; they were biting."

He smirked, but his face was still red.

I put my hand on his shoulder.

"I'm sorry man; I just got backed up."

"That's OK, Doc," he said, letting me off the hook.

I whispered, "Here's a secret; be the first patient here in the morning or the last one in the evening. I'm usually on time for both."

He grinned.

"Thank you, Doctor."

I get that occasionally at my office. People just don't like to wait. I get it. I'm the world's worst at waiting too. I do my best to stay on time, but in family practice, it's pretty difficult. It's especially hard when you practice in the same town that you and your wife grew up in because you know so many of your patients on a personal level. Oh, and by the way, my wife has hundreds of "cousins"!

It seems our whole society is pushing toward a "no waiting" policy. People want things *now*. Not just appointments, but also everything else—products shipped to their home arrive two days; information is downloaded on their phone in seconds; food is delivered to their doorstep in less than an hour. Waiting is a thing of the past!

I told another patient that the only businesses where we have to wait are the doctor's office and the cell phone/computer store. However, when your phone or computer stops working, we are happy to wait in line there. In fact, sometimes we will wait hours for somebody to fix it. Life feels like it is on hold until our device starts working again.

I want to tell you how important it is to have that same attitude about your wait at the doctor's office. I know waiting is aggravating. I know it makes you mad. But Winners Travel to the doctor. I want you to know the benefits that physical health can have on you and your family. I want you to know why you need regular checkups and the latest in diagnostic testing. Your very life may depend on it.

> **Winners Travel to the doctor. I want you to know the benefits that physical health can have on you and your family.**

Let's begin with a story about my daddy. He recently experienced some pain in his left shoulder. I told him to take some Aleve. When it didn't go away, I got him an appointment to see one of my fellow doctors.

"I think it could be his heart," I said to my partner. "He said it kinda hurts in his chest a bit too."

His EKG and labs were normal. All indications were pointing to his shoulder being the source of the pain. But at Colonial Family Practice, we like to think, *What else could it be?* This is especially true for heart disease. I tell patients that the number one killer is the heart, the heart, or the heart.

My partner and I discussed it. Since my dad had multiple risk factors, my partner decided to order a stress test. When he looked at the results, he thought it was a "borderline" positive. Again, he reviewed all the risk factors with my dad and me, and we agreed on a plan. My dad was going to have a heart catheterization with a cardiologist. It would likely be normal, but we didn't want to take a chance.

When the cardiologist walked into the waiting room after the cath, he looked pale. I could barely breathe as he walked over to me.

"Clay, your dad had a 95 percent blockage in his LAD artery. I just put a stent in. He would have been dead in a week if he hadn't come here!"

My mind raced, and I could feel my body going numb. I thought of all the events that had led to my dad having the cath that day. What if I had brushed off his pain as something related to his shoulder? I thought about my practice and all the hard work and consideration that had gone into placing a nuclear stress testing machine in my office. It was a controversial decision, but that machine has saved more lives than any other equipment we have. And when it saves your own father's life, it becomes particularly special. I put my head down and prayed; then I wept.

My dad is still alive today. Yes, he has Alzheimer's disease, but if he could, he would confirm what I'm telling you: You need a physical exam. You need lab work. And you need to get information on the latest testing available to you as a patient and understand what tests are indicated for you and your family. You thought I was going to tell you about diet and exercise here, right? Nope, I'm saving that for later. For now, physical health is about going to your doctor and getting a game plan for routine check-ups, physical exams, and lab work. And yes, that means you might just have to spend some time in waiting rooms!

My partners and I believe that once you reach the age of fifty, you need to have a nuclear stress test. Yes, that's aggressive, but the number one killer is what? The heart, the heart, or . . . the heart. This is true everywhere in the United States, but it is especially true in the South. If the stress test is abnormal or even borderline, you likely need a heart cath. The cath procedure has become much simpler. They essentially put a small catheter, which is a thin tube, in your wrist and float it through the artery into your heart. They squirt dye into the catheter and look at the little arteries that surround the heart. If you have a blockage, the dye stops. If the dye stops, they run a small "straw," called a stent, in there to keep the artery open. If all the main arteries are blocked, the physicians will do a bypass surgery. They will strip a vein from your leg and bypass each blockage. The risks for the surgery have dramatically reduced, and the risks for the stress test and cath are very small. Patients ask me about these risks all the time, and my answer is that a heart attack is by far riskier. I feel that the best way to detect early stage heart disease is through a stress test. Who knows, maybe in the future, we will skip the stress testing and go straight to performing a heart catheterization at age fifty. I would vote for that. I have patients lined up who would tell you the same thing. In the month of March of the year of this book's publication, I saved five lives by being aggressive with heart testing.

I have also put my money where my mouth is. I've had a heart cath of my own. After my dad's scare, I wanted to know about the health of my own heart. I was relieved to learn that my arteries were clear. The procedure was simple. I was back home on my couch by noon the same day, and I worked the next day. With it being that simple, the question really is, why not do it?

OK, so now the big question: How do we prevent heart disease? Well, the jury is still out on this mystery.

One of my best saves is Al Harris. At fifty-eight years old, he was one of the fittest guys one could meet. He had almost zero risk factors and could do one hundred push-ups in a row. In fact, I often asked him for advice on how to increase my push-up count. I could only get to fifty. Because of his age, we pursued heart testing on him, and he had coronary bypass surgery two days later. It amazed me. How did one of the fittest patients I have ever had get severe heart disease? It must be genetic. I think in the next decade we will learn more about that and even have specific genetic testing for heart disease. For now, all we can do is control the basic risk factors. A few of the known ones are: high blood pressure, high cholesterol, smoking, and family history. I aggressively treat these factors now, and I will give you my thoughts on a few of them.

- **High blood pressure is the "silent killer."** It usually has zero symptoms. In medical school, they taught me that the bottom number (the diastolic blood pressure) was the most important. Today, we know the top number (the systolic blood pressure) is the real killer. *Ouch.* Remember earlier when I said that 50 percent of what I learned in medical school was wrong?

  We do know that the goal is to get the top number below 140. So how do you know what your top number is? You could check it yourself, but I know most people don't . . . or won't. They usually wait to be told during their physical or when they have a cold. That's another feather in the cap of going to get a checkup: you are told your systolic number. After that, you can buy your own cuff and start checking it at different times of the day. If your average top number is high, please go see your doctor again. It matters. Blood pressure in the United States is entirely too high! In fact, the more I read about and study it, I predict the top number should be less than 120. All the studies are beginning to point that way, and elevated blood pressure is a huge risk factor for heart attack and stroke. One recent study I read even implicated high blood pressure as a risk factor for Alzheimer's disease.[1] We need clear-cut proof, but I feel we will learn a lot more in the next few years about the ideal level of blood pressure. Winners, get yours checked today.

- **The second and most well-known risk factor is high cholesterol.** Most people think high cholesterol is related to a high-fat diet, so they vow to change their diet and lose weight. What they mean is, they will try a popular diet for six months and then recheck their cholesterol. Even if they lose weight and eat perfectly, their level rarely comes down. They fuss at me, but I recommend a statin for all

---

[1] R.F. Gottesman, M.S. Albert, A. Alonso, L.H. Coker, J. Coresh, S.M. Davis, J.A Deal, et al, "Associations Between Midlife Vascular Risk Factors and 25-Year Incident Dementia in the Atherosclerosis Risk in Communities (ARIC) Cohort," *JAMA Neurology*, October 2017, 74(10): 1246–1254, doi: 10.1001/jamaneurol.2017.1658.

those with elevated lousy cholesterol, or LDL. Statins are a family of medicines that show solid evidence that they reduce stroke and heart attack by a large percentage. I once saw an obese, 300-pound guy, and his total cholesterol was 180. The same day, I saw a fit, 120-pound young girl who mainly ate a vegetarian diet, and her cholesterol was over 320! It all makes sense that cholesterol is in your genes, not your food. Even the cardiologists I know with high cholesterol take statins, and so do I. Please go get your cholesterol checked, and find out your number.

- **Smoking is the third obvious risk factor.** I will discuss in a later chapter my best recommendation for quitting successfully. Start planting that seed today that you will quit smoking. There is a medicine out there now that can help you. I believe it's a gateway medicine, and it will open the door for new therapies for all kinds of addiction in the future. Once again, to take care of your physical health, you need to take a trip to the doctor to stay up on the latest and greatest advances.

- **Last but not least is your family history.** I know that this is not something you can control, but knowing the cards you've been dealt can help you to take appropriate action. I strongly recommend you obtain an understanding of your family history of heart disease (and for that matter, any other diseases), and be conscious of them. Facing the reality of your family history is difficult, I know, but instead of letting it cripple you or make you feel helpless, allow it to empower you. You can use it to make decisions that will support a healthy lifestyle so that you can live the best version of yourself, despite the hand you've been dealt.

So those are the basics on what causes heart disease. I'd like to cover one more common condition: cancer. Cancer has many forms and causes, but certain ones are so much more manageable if we catch them early. When I see patients in the office for any reason, I always take the opportunity to ask about cancer screening tests. For women, I recommend a mammogram every year after age thirty-five. I know, I know; I've never had my boobs squashed by a machine before. But mammograms unequivocally save lives. The treatment is so advanced that we can handle most breast cancers if we catch them early. Go to the doctor, and get a mammogram every year.

Colon cancer is also curable if caught early. The national age recommendation for a colonoscopy is fifty, but truthfully, I feel that's too late. I have had two friends die in their forties from colon cancer. If it were up to me, I'd change the national recommendation to forty years of age. The medicine we use for sedation during colonoscopies has improved it so much that a rare few are conscious of the fact that I'm in there doing what needs to be done. Don't let the thought of the procedure put you off. I had my first one when I was forty-two. Winners don't ignore this one.

Men, the prostate is in a bad place. I don't like to check it either, but a digital rectal exam helps with early detection of prostate cancer. I also use the PSA blood test. It is a reliable test, and it's especially helpful to compare the number from your result when performed yearly after age fifty. Please get a PSA every year after you turn fifty.

The only other cancer screening tool that reliably works is a CAT scan of the chest to look for lung cancer. In fact, Medicare even covers this test yearly for smokers. If you find a lung nodule around the size of a dime, we can usually treat it. However, if it's the size of a quarter, it's often too late. If you smoke, plan to quit, and go get a CAT scan.

These are the basics that I recommend for Winners Traveling to physical health. Did I say to go get a physical? Of course. Technology is rapidly advancing, so you'll want to stay up on it, because over the next several years, the medical community will have more and more technology to assist with diagnoses and treatment.

I believe that one of the main reasons Colonial Family Practice is so successful is that we are "preventers." It is what we practice. In the old days, you went to your doctor when you were sick. Now, you should be going so you *won't get* sick. We try to prevent catastrophes by being aggressive with technology. It matters if you discover things early! But the only way you'll discover things early is if you make your health a priority, take the time to schedule regular checkups, and engage with your doctor.

We do all sorts of diagnostics in our office. We offer colonoscopies, endoscopies, CAT scans, MRI procedures, stress testing, and echocardiograms. We also offer full lab work and even perform sleep testing. It seems that this "one-stop shopping" is desirable to our patients, and it's catching on. Patients are much more likely to undergo these lifesaving tests if they are offered the opportunity to have them all performed in one convenient, trusted location.

I know a young man who will attest to that. He's my little nephew, Tillman. He was ten at the time of this story—large for his age, with blond hair and a wide, toothy grin. His mother, Jordan, brought him in for a headache. My physician's assistant, Kim Reisenauer, saw him while I was out of the office one Wednesday afternoon. We had just installed the CAT scanner the day before. Kim ordered a scan on Tillman and called me in horror with the results. He had a malignant brain tumor. I came into Sumter from our home in Mayesville to tell Jordan in person. These conversations are far from the best part of my job, and no matter how many times I have to have them, they never get easier.

We got Tillman to a neurosurgeon immediately. Within a week, he was admitted into the hospital and awaiting surgery. The surgeon came out after about seven hours of brain surgery and said he had to "extirpate" the entire tumor. I had to Google what that meant, but in Southern terms, it means, he got it all!

Tillman went on to live a normal life and became a star football lineman. Man, I loved watching him play football, and I always think about that day and how he might not be here if it were not for our CAT scanner. We might not win them all, but it is good to have a chance!

So my challenge to you is to take control of your physical health. You can do it! Get educated. I get a lot of pushback on time and costs, but my answer always goes back to The Wealth Formula. Remember, if you lose the 1, then all the 0s behind it don't matter.

CHAPTER 11

# Winners Travel
# to Mental Health

*"The one surefire way to cure depression
is to find somebody who needs help and help them!"*
— Clay Lowder

JOAN DID NOT EVEN LOOK at me as I bounced into the exam room. I smiled the best I could and tried my traditional line: "What's happening?" Her lip quivered, and she started crying immediately.

"I have the worst headache ever!" she screamed. "It's a twelve on a scale of one to ten! I have had it for three weeks, and I cannot work. I'm nauseated. You need to fix it!"

I took a deep breath and eased into my questions. I started from the beginning. Her interview revealed the following: She had severe joint aches and neck pain, mainly at night, with numbness and tingling all over. She also had blurred vision and complained of reflux. All of her physical exam results were normal except for moderately baggy lower eyelids. I ran a lab panel and decided to do a quick CAT scan of her head. Most doctors do a CAT scan when patients say, "This is the worst headache of my life." Sometimes it can indicate an aneurysm, and it's *always* good to catch those early.

The CAT scan and all the labs were normal. I gave her some migraine medicine and a prescription for prednisone, a steroid. One of my first mentors in family medicine, Dr. John Little, taught me that trick. It breaks the cycle of a severe headache. As my daughter, Liza, always says, "If my dad isn't sure what to do, he gives you prednisone."

I followed up with Joan the next week. She was clearly worse. She wanted to see a neurologist pronto! I was tempted to just send her to Dr. John Baker, our Colonial neurologist, but something just did not add up.

I told Joan, "Hey, when things don't add up, I usually look for other causes. Can I ask you some more questions first?"

"Sure," she said reluctantly.

I had a feeling I knew what was wrong, but I needed to ease into it. I started with sleep.

"Are you sleeping OK?"

"Well, not really," she replied. "I often wake up around four in the morning and can't go back to sleep."

"How long has that been going on?" I asked.

"About three weeks."

"All right. Have you felt tired?"

I knew the answer; everyone is tired. But I had a plan.

"I am exhausted!" she exclaimed. "Could it be my thyroid?

I wish I had a nickel for every time someone asked me about their thyroid.

"How about your nerves. Have they been bad?" I asked.

"Well, not really," she stammered.

I think she realized where I was going. Then she kind of tucked her head and looked away.

"Well, maybe I have been somewhat stressed," she admitted.

After about another ten questions, her guard was coming down.

"Has anyone in your family ever had depression?" I asked.

"Well, yes. My mother and my sister. They take medication for it."

Almost universally, depression runs in families. I decided to go for it.

I said, "Well my family has it too. In fact, it's pretty strong. I had no idea I had it until I went to medical school."

That disarmed her. She let her guard down completely, and tears began to fall.

"Well, there is a lot of stress on me, and it's starting to get to me. I guess I am depressed."

Wow. The first step is acceptance. At that point, I knew we were headed somewhere.

"I can help you to battle this disease," I said. "I recommend three things. One is medication. I am giving you an antidepressant, which you should take for six months to a year. I am also going to give you a sleeping pill called Ambien, which I want you to take for three nights. It will break this sleep cycle, which will help your headaches immediately. The second therapy is exercise. Everyone knows exercise helps you physically, but I am telling you, it helps you more mentally. You have to get those "cobwebs" out of your brain. You cannot beat a good sweat to do that. It doesn't have to be a lot. Just begin with a brisk, ten-minute walk, and start today. The third part of my plan is my surefire way to cure depression. It is this: find someone who needs help, and help them! It doesn't have to be much, just go visit someone in the hospital, cook someone a meal, or even mow someone's lawn. I have found it to be one of the best ways to make me feel better about myself. I am so thankful I have a job in which the Lord sends me a new person each day who needs my help. So that is it, Joan. Three things. One: medicine. Two: exercise. And three: help someone."

I told her that if she did all three, her headaches and depression would improve.

She came back to my office two weeks later. When I entered the room this time, I was shocked. She was standing and pacing around, but when she saw me, she pounced! She grabbed me and wrapped me in a big bear hug. I could barely breathe. She was feeling so much better and was so eager to tell me all about the meal she had made for Joe, her neighbor. She said the headaches were all but gone, and she was sleeping through the night. The therapy was working, and she did not mention the neurologist again. Man, I *love* being a doctor!

You would not believe how many patients we see with anxiety and depression. Many of them are convinced there is something physically wrong with them because they haven't even considered that it could be mental. Most come in with physical symptoms, and I have to pull it out of them. Some will admit it flat out, but for most, I have to gain their trust first. The best way for me to do this is to build a relationship with them by asking caring questions, and soon, they will tell me everything.

At my office we employ a lot of counseling as well. We even have our own counselor, Day Caughman, to help us work with these patients.

I was talking to my partner, Dr. Dave Whaley, the other day. He said he had four straight patients with depression, and when he met with his next patient, she said, "All I need, Dr. Whaley, is a Z-Pak!"

"Whew!" he sighed, and started to write out a prescription for the antibiotic.

When he looked up, she was crying and said, "I just found out my husband is leaving me! I am so depressed!"

It's hard to be a doctor all day, hearing statements like this. I just want to help everybody who comes through my door. Sometimes my day is a roller coaster of emotions; I can go from being happy and confident during one visit to feeling aggravated or confused during the next. It's a challenge, but in the end, when I have the privilege of helping somebody find a solution to his or her problem, it's a rewarding feeling.

I have always encouraged my kids to be intentional about finding those who need help. It is a good policy even if you are not depressed. I want them to have perspective. You might be wondering how helping others can help you mentally, especially if you're depressed and may not even feel like doing something for *yourself*. Well, I believe it displaces your negative thoughts. By helping others, you are forcing your brain to push those thoughts aside and instead focus on the person you are helping. Afterward, you feel so great about making somebody else smile that it typically makes you smile too.

Don't let anybody fool you; everyone who breathes has negative thoughts. Those of us with depression may just have them more often. You have to learn how to get rid of them. They come to me too. Most of the time they are automatic and out of the blue. Mine sound like this: *You suck. You missed that diagnosis. You are an hour behind. Your patients don't like you.* Bam! Where do those thoughts come from?

> **Don't let anybody fool you; everyone who breathes has negative thoughts. You just have to learn how to get rid of them.**

For several years, I used a cool trick. I put a rubber band on my wrist, and every time my mind went haywire with these negative thoughts, I'd snap the rubber band. Then I'd repeat to myself, *You are OK. You are all right. God is in charge of your life. You are the best doctor. You are doing the Lord's work. Now go into the next exam room, and look the patient square in the eyes, and do your best.*

Winners, consider trying the rubber band trick for your own mental health management. I'm sure it is one of the cheapest treatments you've ever heard of. It will literally "snap" you back into reality and help you displace all those negative thoughts. It's also an eye-opening way to discover just how many negative thoughts can creep in over the course of just one day. After a year or so, I got so good at it that I didn't need the rubber band anymore. I was able to instantly recognize these thoughts the second they started to flood in, and I could quickly course-correct. My wrist felt better too!

So, other than a rubber band, what else do Winners need for mental health? I didn't prescribe this to Joan, who I mentioned previously, because I had my own set of plans for her, but I have another cheap, simple tool to help you get rid of your bad thoughts. And this one is important. It's called reading. I mean reading books—good books. I fear that in this day and age, reading is a lost art. Most young people don't read at all. I hope to change that.

How does reading a good book change the way you think? Similar to the rubber band trick, it forces your brain to think differently. When you read stories of people who are way less fortunate than you, it shows you that you don't have it so bad. Stories about people who succeed in business may inspire you to finally pursue your dreams of opening up that cupcake shop or website-building business. Reading gives you somebody with whom you can identify. It's called gaining perspective. When an author makes decisions that change his or her life against all odds, it can motivate you. The key is to *actually* read though; don't speed read just to finish the book and say you read it. You have to go slowly and carefully process the material; that's the only way you will come away from reading a book feeling as if it has improved your mental state. Reading also calms the brain and soothes the soul. I highly recommend reading at night when you first climb into bed. For some reason, it helps with sleep. Your TV and phone are so stimulating that they can keep you up for hours. If you are suffering from insomnia and/or depression, then get a good book, and give it a shot each night at bedtime. Even if you can only read for five minutes at first, just try it. I guarantee you that you'll fall asleep faster, sleep more soundly, and feel more inspired day in and day out.

I write prescriptions for books all the time. In fact, I have a stack of good reads in my office that I give out regularly. When I'm counseling a patient for depression, sometimes I just get a feeling that they need a book. I'll grab one out of my office and ask them to read it. They are usually so shocked by this off-the-wall "prescription" that they don't know what to say at first, but they leave the office with the book, and when they come back for their next visit, I'm usually greeted with a story and a thank you. Giving someone in need a book is also another way of "finding someone who needs help and helping them." It's simple and cheap, and everyone can do it. Give it a try for your own mental health. Get some copies of your favorite book, and send it to someone who you think could use it.

My wife's cousin Brandon Kinder and his wife, Danielle, taught me that trick. They sent Kelliegh and me a copy of *The Noticer* and *The Noticer Returns* by Andy Andrews years ago. Andy is a storyteller. In fact, I argue that he's America's best storyteller. These books will change your life if you truly absorb the information in them. Kelliegh and I read them as a couple, and we had the deepest conversations we'd ever had after reading them. We were so changed by them that we've ordered copies by the case; we have hundreds of them at home. Kelliegh even gave them out as graduation gifts to all the members of our kids' high school graduating classes. She is a real giver.

So reading books is a way to help others and yourself mentally. Try Andy Andrews first. When you want to discover more titles, see www.claylowder.com for my reading list.

My mother used to make us read for thirty minutes each day on our family summer vacation trips to Santee Lakes. I protested then, but now I know why she had us do this. You were right again, Mom.

I believe in the power of the written word so much that I used to pay my kids to read books! I once read this quote, "A wise man learns from experience. A super-wise man learns from the experience of others!" So read, read, read!

Last but certainly not least, I believe that one more thing you can do to help mitigate depression and negative thoughts is to help others. There is something fulfilling in knowing that you have helped somebody you know, or even a stranger, have a better day. It can be as simple as smiling at somebody in the grocery store or calling a friend just to talk, to more time-consuming things like helping a friend move or renovate their home. Selfless acts that are

> **The one surefire way to cure depression is to find somebody who needs help and help them!**

meant to make somebody else's life easier, less painful, and just happier, will keep you feeling full of personal harmony longer than anything else.

That's why helping others is just one of my many passions. I've always admired former Clemson quarterback Deshaun Watson, and watched the way he grew, not only as a quarterback, but also as a servant leader. He learned from two great men, Coach Dabo Swinney and my brother Dr. Milt Lowder, how to be a real man while he was at Clemson. He went on to donate his first NFL paycheck to three cafeteria workers in Houston. I love it!

I really do believe that deep down, we all want to help others, but some of us just do not know how or do not have the means to do it. That's one reason why I decided to start the Winners Travel Foundation. As I speak and write, I want to donate to this foundation. The Winners Travel

Foundation's purpose is to identify people who have given throughout their entire lives but have not taken much for themselves. My main focus is on caretakers. I think back to my mom taking care of my grandma; she gave up many days and nights to be there with my grandma. My foundation affords everybody the opportunity to decide how they'd like to give and when.

Kelliegh and I have gifted trips many times over the years, and we love to see the look on the other person's face when we surprise them and their family with a fancy trip. Most recently, we went to see Rose, a lady who is a caretaker for her son Jacobby. Jacobby is twenty-six years old now and has had issues since birth. This woman has dedicated her whole life to Jacobby, and she really cannot go anywhere. She is always there for him.

At Christmas, I took my family to Rose's house, and we surprised her with a trip to New York City. She was blown away! Now, I am not good at Instachat or Snapgram (I'm just being silly; I know they're called Instagram and Snapchat), but I do have a video of the Christmas surprise on my Facebook page and website. You have got to see her reaction!

I loved the idea so much of giving away trips to people who have dedicated their lives to helping others that I decided to start my foundation so that it could be done on a much larger scale and with involvement by people everywhere.

If you help someone like Rose and Jacobby, or know someone who does, feel free to nominate them for a surprise Winners Travel Award. Go to www.winnerstravel.org, and post your story!

# CHAPTER 12

# Winners Travel to Spiritual Health

*"Your brain is a computer,*
*and God has a plan for your life."*
— Dr. Jennie Ariail

I GOT C'S ON MY FIRST two tests in medical school. I was always able to maintain good grades, so it was a hard pill for me to swallow. I was down; I was distraught. I had never received C's before. As my daughter, Liza, would say, "What to do, what to do, what to do?"

I finally broke down and called my mom, Dr. Jennie Ariail.

She began to pepper me with questions: "How late are you staying up? What time are you getting up?"

It did not take her long to figure it out. I was staying up late studying, waking up late, and barely making it to class on time. I was unkempt and unshaven.

"Clay, you are trying too hard! You need to stop worrying. Go to bed now. Get up early, drink some coffee, sit up front in class, and take furious notes."

I gasped. It was only 9:00 p.m., and I had not gone to bed that early in years. She was right. I had been using the preprinted notes they had given us and hadn't been writing out notes of my own. Then she told me something I have never forgotten.

"Clay, your brain is a computer, and God has a plan for your life," she said.

I sighed, and she said it again, nice and slowly. I felt better and more relaxed. *What the heck,* I thought. I decided to give her advice a shot. I was already getting C's, so I figured it wouldn't hurt to try something new. What was the worst thing that could happen?

"Thanks, Mom!" I said before hanging up.

Following my mom's suggestions, I started to go to bed early, get up early, prepare for the day, and take notes like crazy. Sure enough, the C's went away. I went on to figure it out and had a successful medical school career. Now, when I start to stress, I close my eyes and remember that quote from my mom. I have even turned it into my own prayer. I remind myself over and over again that God has a plan for my life.

I am a practicing Christian. As discussed in Chapter 6, I have seen firsthand many miracles in my career that had absolutely no scientific reason for them to occur other than God. In fact, one of them was my lifelong family friend's mom. She was in the ICU with a pelvic cancer that was incurable. She started bleeding, and I mean *bleeding*. It was pouring out of her as if someone had turned on a faucet! I was doing my best, adding blood into her IV and packing her wound over and over. She never complained. I stopped and had a word with her in private.

"I don't think I can give you enough blood," I said. "I am so sorry."

She cut me off, "Clay, keep giving me the blood. I am going to see my son for Christmas."

One of her sons was on the West Coast and would not be in town for another two weeks for Christmas.

"I don't think that is going to work," I said as gently as I could. "I am sorry."

I usually try to be as frank with my patients as I can and tell them the truth, as I would want someone to do with me.

She looked up at me with a tear in her eye and said, "No sir, I'm going to live until I see my son."

When I sighed and turned my head, she continued, "Clay, I have talked to God, and He told me."

I went on to protest again, but something hit me. I went to get more blood.

This struggle went on all night. Her hemoglobin went all the way down to two, while a normal level is twelve. I have never seen it that low. You just cannot live at two! Well, live she did. Not only did she make it to Christmas, she lived another three months. We were able to fit some sweet family time in there, and everybody got to say a proper goodbye. It does not always go this way, but there is no medical reason for a person to live through that. I can still see the gleam in her eye when her son walked in and she said to me, "I told you so!"

Not only does spiritual health produce miracles, I believe it can also help you heal in other ways. True health is a blend of the physical, mental, and spiritual. I put that on the back of my first brochure, which I handed to patients in 1996, and I've preached it ever since. Everybody likes to talk about the first two types of health, but it can be difficult to start a conversation about spiritual health. When I get my patients to open up about it, it's typically a rewarding feeling for us both. At some point in life, most of us have experienced some kind of unexplained spiritual moment. We have felt guided to a path we hadn't previously wanted to take. If I can get a patient to relive that moment, they usually get a chill. Often, their eyes start to tear up. They exhale. They begin to heal. It's a process, and I love to get it started.

Winners traveling to true health must also include some kind of spiritual health in their game plan. If fought, it will work against the body's natural healing response. It's not that God is out to get you; in fact, it's the opposite. He wants to help you. He wants you to feel love. Love is the strongest human emotion, and the mind and body crave it. When humans feel love, they change.

> **Winners traveling to true health must also include some kind of spiritual health in their game plan.**

They grow. The body relaxes. A cascade of healing chemicals is activated. It is the culmination of health.

One of my favorite verses in the Bible is Philippians 4:13. It says, "I can do all things through Christ, who gives me strength." It doesn't say *one* thing; it says *all* things. I tell this to almost all of my patients. Sometimes they are going through tough times, and they need faith and guidance to keep going. In my experience, the ones who embrace it move on. They gain a deeper perspective and leave my office with an understanding of the importance of spiritual health. I'll say it again: spiritual health is a must.

Now, some doctors don't recognize the value of spiritual health. They are strict believers in science and science only. I believe in science as well, but the more I experience, the more I am convinced that we also have a creator. I've seen faith and prayer turn things around that science just couldn't fix.

Did you know that people who attend church can live up to seven years longer than those who don't? They actually did a study on this. Good spiritual health[1] seems to be tied to longevity.

I encourage my patients to find a home church. It is comforting to have people who love you, and in a time when many of us are suffering from family relationship issues, a church can fill that void. A good church will help you and your family in a time of need. It's something you can count on and something you can believe in. I think that's healthy.

Do you need healing in your life? Do you need relationships saved? Do you want to be truly healthy? Start working on your spiritual life. Here's an easy way to start. When you first wake up in the morning, look out your window and say a quick prayer—something like, "Hey, Lord, good morning. Thank you for this sunrise. Thank you for this view." Thank Him for the first things you see and the first few things that pop into your mind. Then read a quick devotional, a Bible

---

[1] Lydia Strohl, "Why Doctors Now Believe Faith Heals," *Reader's Digest,* May 2001, 109–115.

verse, or even a paragraph of a spiritual book. A good one is Og Mandino's *The Greatest Salesman in the World*. Read one of the scrolls. They are brief. Then, as your day evolves and everything hits the fan, you can think about the words you read that morning. Have a brief conversation with the Lord again. I say, "I'm OK; I'm all right. Help me, Lord." Remember, "Your brain is a computer, and God has a plan for your life!"

# CHAPTER 13

# Winners Travel to Quitting Bad Habits

*"I have failed over and over and over again in my life.*
*And that is why I succeed."*
— Michael Jordan

I HAVE A POSTER IN MY office of Michael Jordan, and it contains this quote.

Most days I read it, then look him in the eye and say, "If you can fail, buddy—over and over again, then so can I."

Winners get up. They never, ever quit. My dad taught me that at a very young age. It was a Lowder principle.

Once, I told him that I wanted to quit basketball.

"Fine," he said. "Be at work at 3:00 p.m., right after school."

> **Winners get up. They never, ever quit. My dad taught me that at a very young age. It was a Lowder principle.**

Needless to say, I kept dribbling.

Most people give up on bad habits, especially when it comes to weight loss and smoking. I have found that with a little coaching, I can help almost anyone.

Everyone knows that smoking is bad for you and will shorten your life. I have a method that will help you or your loved one quit. I will share it with you at the end of this chapter. However, I feel there's an even more dangerous habit out there. I think we will learn in the future that food kills more people than all other vices combined. We have an obesity epidemic in our country, and I've seen first-hand the negative effects that weight gain and an unhealthy relationship with food have on the body. So in order to fix this, we have to have a game plan for food too. We have to break our addiction to it. Here is my recipe for how to do so. It is called the Fuel Diet.

The Fuel Diet is a simple diet that I have developed, and it works. I have helped hundreds of people lose twenty pounds or more, some up to one hundred pounds. It is easy and it does not require starvation. My theory is that your body needs "fuel" to survive. When it runs low, it goes into protection mode. It holds on to the best energy storage it has: fat. In order to burn fat and not store it, you need to do the opposite of what is prescribed by most diets. You need to eat! Sounds good, right? Here are the key points:

1.  Understand that this is not a diet. It is a lifestyle change.

2.  Eat six times a day! Eat a big breakfast and a light supper, and eat every two hours in between.

3.  If you wait until you are hungry to eat, it is too late. You are storing fat.

4.  Eat at 4:00 p.m. This is my number one weight-loss tip. You have to limit supper, so eat up at 4:00 p.m. If you don't listen to anything else I say, try this step. It works.

5.  Drink water. Start with sipping ice water all day and with each meal. You will soon become addicted to it.

## The Fuel Diet Sample Meal Plan

### Breakfast

- A one-to-four–egg omelet with a small amount of cheese
- Black coffee (with or without stevia/cinnamon)
- Ice water

### 10 a.m. Snack

- One of the following:
  - ◊ Two pieces of ready-made bacon
  - ◊ Ice water/coffee

◊ A handful of almonds or peanuts

- Ice water/coffee

## Lunch

- Sandwich or hamburger (but throw away the bun)

- Celery sticks with hummus (no chips)

Salads are good, but no dressing except oil and vinegar. No bread!

## 2 p.m. Snack

- A few leftovers from lunch (remember, you are not hungry), almonds, peanuts, cheese stick, jerky

## 4 p.m. Key Snack

- An apple is my go-to.

- A few alternatives: a boiled egg, peanuts, almonds, jerky

Eat as much as you can. Your mother said, "Don't eat that! It will ruin your appetite!" Your doctor says, "Exactly!"

## Supper

- A small amount of fish, chicken, or steak

- Vegetables: all you can eat

## Last but not least, Dessert!

- This is a must, especially in the South. One small piece of dark chocolate, a strawberry, and some low-carb Cool Whip

Dessert tells my brain that I am done—no seconds. Eat it as early as you can.

**Foods to Avoid:** Bread, rice, pasta, cereal, sweet drinks, alcohol

**Foods to Limit:** Fruits (except apples), yogurt

**All You Can Eat:** Protein, lean meats, vegetables, nuts

Using the five key points mentioned above along with this meal plan, you will be well on your way to losing weight. If you are serious about your health and weight loss, set a goal weight today, and write it on your mirror—for example, "I am going to weigh 150 pounds by June 1."

If you've built your goal board out, include pictures on it that help you visualize what you want to do—maybe it's to wear a certain outfit or have visible biceps or get a new hairstyle. Then start to take action! My good buddy Dr. Michael Chestnut says, "Be an athlete!" That means prepare, plan, and focus. Athletes don't just go out on the field sans preparation. Their entire lives are prepared from the moment they start their morning workouts to the food they eat throughout the day to the time they go to sleep.

I also believe that you should exercise in some way every day. It does not have to be for an hour! In fact, a recent article I read said that too much cardio can be bad for you. I only do ten minutes every other day. I do "HIIT"—High-Intensity Interval Training. In its most basic form, it works like this: Walk for two minutes, and then sprint for thirty seconds. Repeat.

Then quit at ten minutes. I do this when I am cleaning up the garage or going to the barn. Make simple everyday tasks your exercise. If you have been around me for a minute, you will have seen that I live it. I like to hustle and do not have much time for exercise, so these are my opportunities. My kids have heard me say a million times, "Run everywhere you go" and "Walk 25 percent faster!" I urge you to start doing this today.

My last piece of advice about weight loss is to compete with yourself. How? Weigh yourself every day. Then get up and pee (sorry, Mom), and get "buck naked." Weigh yourself again. If you have gained a pound, eliminate from your plan the food you ate the day before. If you've lost a pound, "repeat eat!"

I have found that humans can eat basically the same thing for five out of seven days. You can lose a pound a day, which works out to five pounds a week! In this way, you are auditing your food plan and competing with yourself to lose a pound. After a while, you will know exactly what to eat in a day to lose one. You will figure out that magic formula that allows you to eat more and weigh less! And you will still get to enjoy food.

I recently returned from traveling to San Francisco, where I watched my Clemson Tigers win the National Championship. I am not going to lie, I celebrated. My brother Milt Lowder is the team's sport psychologist, and I was so proud to share a "Moment with Milt." So, when I returned home after eating bread and drinking a few beers (I am not perfect!), I found

I had gained five pounds in four days. See, it happens faster than you think! But after just four days of following the Fuel Diet and being consistent in my physical activity, I had already lost it again.

I know, I know, you have failed over and over with weight management. Welcome to the club. Now take a ticket, and get in line. What do you have to lose? Nothing. Give the Fuel Diet a try.

Now that we have a food game plan, I want to share my method for quitting smoking. This method can work for all bad habits. You *can* do it!

My sister, Candler, is a person of action. She wanted to quit smoking; she just did not know how. We had a little session and talked about goal-setting 101. We agreed she would write her goal on her mirror, adding some urgency and emotion to it (set a solid date to be done, and include a loved one in her plan), and we got her some medication.

In November, she wrote in giant letters on her mirror:

I AM GOING TO QUIT SMOKING ON FEBRUARY 3 BECAUSE I LOVE CHARLIE BHAT!

I gave her a prescription for Chantix. It is a nicotine-receptor blocker that eventually makes you sick on nicotine if you take it long enough. People push back on it, but the only two side effects are mild nausea and vivid dreams. It does not inspire suicide or make you crazy. It does not cause nightmares; it just makes you not like cigarettes. It also prevents you from gaining weight. She bought into it and wanted to be "all in!"

I coached her to read her goal aloud every day, which she did. And she went one step further: she boldly told all of her friends she was quitting, and even posted it on Facebook. If you want something really bad, tell it to the world on Facebook. It is like lighting a fire.

People said to my sister, "OMG, you won't do it!"

"Oh yes, I will!" she retorted.

It became something of a dare, and as you already know by now, the Lowders love to prove what they're capable of!

And guess what? Candler stopped smoking on February 3. She is two years out now, and I am so proud of her—but not as proud as her son, Charlie (my shark-fishing partner)!

In order to quit any habit, you can use the following technique:

1. Write down your goal. A goal is just a wish floating around unless it's written!

2. Add urgency and emotion. Set a date, like your child's birthday, and add, "BECAUSE I LOVE _____." And then tell the world.

3. Use other tactics, including medication, counseling, and electronic reminders.

Be a person of action. Do it today. Please! Winners cannot travel if they cannot breathe.

Remember, if Michael Jordan has failed, so can we. Don't let past failures get in your way of a Winners Travel life of health. Don't let a food or cigarette addiction control you. Get a game plan today.

# CHAPTER 14

# Winners Travel to Financial Health

*"Your money should be like a big fullback blocking for you!"*
— Clayton Lowder Sr.

M Y GRANDDADDY WAS A SELF-MADE man. He was the youngest of nine children and grew up in tough times. He became an entrepreneur at an early age and turned a tiny gas station business into a Red & White grocery store, the Pig Inn restaurant, a cotton gin, and a huge cattle farm. Unfortunately, he had several divorces and ended up with little to show for all his hard work.

We were always close; I even worked with him one summer. I asked him one day for his best financial advice, and I have never forgotten what he told me.

"If another woman propositions you, tuck your tail and run, boy!"

If you think about it, that's pretty good financial advice these days. I have always followed that rule.

> **Why is financial advice important to the concept of Winners Travel? Because those who struggle financially let their finances affect their mental health.**

Why is financial advice important to the concept of Winners Travel? I find that those who struggle financially let their finances affect their mental health. I am not a financial expert, but I have learned from years of mistakes. I thought I would include some nuggets of wisdom here.

I have a talk I give kids in high school and college. It is called the "Top Ten Things I Wish I'd Known in School." Here they are (though they are not in any particular order):

1. **Plan to be rich.**

2. **Save 10 percent and tithe 10 percent.** Give until it hurts. My grandmother, Jane Ariail, taught me this one. Even when she was in a nursing home with severe Parkinson's disease, she demanded my mother tithe

all her checks, even her tax refund. I have done that since receiving my very first check. It is a kind of "pay yourself first" plan. Here's our recurring theme: have a game plan. You need a financial plan. Most folks just get their paycheck and hold on to as much as they can. It ends up being very little that way. I have another way to save money (see the next point).

3. **Set up three bank accounts.** Figure out 10 percent of your monthly income, and set up direct deposits into your other accounts on the first of the month. One account is your tithing account, where you'll send 10 percent of your paycheck. The other is a savings account, where another 10 percent will go. Then hire a broker—like TD Ameritrade or a local broker—to invest the amount added to that savings account on a monthly basis. My best advice is to do what Warren Buffett says: "Invest in America; it works!" Your third account is where the rest of your money will go.

I would listen to him. I would buy no-load or low-cost ETFs or mutual funds in American companies, and plan to hold them "forever." Both sound scary, but they are just groups of stocks. Stocks are simply a small-percentage ownership of businesses. I feel the best businesses in the world are right here in the United States. You don't have to worry about picking individual stocks or even knowing anything about the stock market. Using a company like the one mentioned above means that a broker will evaluate the stocks, pick a couple of groups of stocks, and plan on holding them. Remember, it's only 10 percent. You cannot rush the process, and you cannot require access to the money at any time in the immediate future. This is a long-term plan.

The stocks in the group earn interest each year. I did not know that at first. It's called a dividend. It's like making money while you sleep. Each year the interest is added to your account. I suggest you reinvest the interest in your group of stocks. Then the interest starts earning interest. It's minimal over the first few years, but after ten years, it starts to really increase. You should see it after twenty years! If you are patient, it will absolutely skyrocket in forty years. Young people, listen to me here. Even if you make a small amount of money, you can easily become a millionaire this way. It's called compound interest. You just need time, interest, and American companies (stocks). That "interest-earning interest" is like having your own big, burly fullback blocking for you! In addition to the "tuck your tail and run" method, this was my granddaddy's advice.

4.  **My best advice is for you to get a "financial educa-tion."** I have read hundreds of books on investing, and I have practiced and refined what we do in terms of it. We certainly educate our children today, but this kind of education isn't included. You will have to teach yourself. I've included a few sources at the end of this book to get you started.

You should also teach your kids to invest. They need to do so. Let them learn *with* you and then *from* you. I believe it is our responsibility to teach our kids, as we are leaving our legacy to them. Here's a saying that really speaks to me: "The dead bird under the nest is the one that never learned to fly." It makes me think about how to handle my kids and help them prepare to successfully venture out into the world on their own.

5. **My next piece of advice is to pay for your kids' education until they are twenty or so (you decide), and that is it.** Cut them off at that point. Do not worry; it is good for them. (I'll admit, I have not done this perfectly, but I am trying now.) When you complete your life plan and become wealthy, consider a "generation-skipping trust," where your money goes to your grandkids' education. Usually, it is the school of hard knocks that has made us great, so why deny that opportunity to the ones you love the most? Start teaching your kids today.

6. **Another financial consideration is to go into business for yourself.** To me, this is the American dream. I would like all young people to think of ways they can do this. You are in control, and the success of your finances is determined by you and the hard work you put into your business—plain and simple. Nothing will teach you more about life and other people than having your

butt on the line as you're running your own business. Yes, you will make some mistakes. I have learned from my mistakes more than my successes. One of them is filling a position with an average person in order to speed up the hiring process. Doing so will bite you in the long run. My goal now is to hire the best people no matter how long it takes. I have a message on my wall that says, "Surround yourself with great people, and you will be great." That statement has catapulted Colonial Family Practice to the top.

I have accomplished this by surrounding myself with great doctors. People call me an entrepreneur, and they always ask how we grew Colonial Family Practice to be so large. First of all, I have great partners. They are all like-minded, hard-working doctors who look patients in the eye and take care of them. It's rare today for doctors to own their own practices and work for themselves. *We* do. We started with a motto: "We will see you today!" When you work for yourself, you will gladly see more customers.

Scheduling same-day appointments seems like a no-brainer, but most doctors will not do so. Therefore, "We will see you today!" became our mind-set and our unique selling feature that set us apart from the competition. We also put it in place to remind our providers and staff to do our best to take care of people *today*. It has been a fantastic business concept for us.

One of the best things to happen to Colonial was that Dr. Dave Whaley, Dr. Mitch Grunsky, and I got colonoscopy trained. We needed a gastrointestinal suite. I heard that one existed at Dillon Family Medicine, so I went to Dillon, South Carolina, to see it. When I got there, Dr. Doug Jenkins showed me around. He showed me his CT scanner and full lab. I was blown away. It was like a mini hospital! I hadn't realized it was possible to have all of that equipment in one place. I got every representative's phone number, and I was off to the races. Once you expand your mind like that, you can hardly rein it back in!

7. **I call this business model the "copycat."** Plain and simple, it works. In fact, I just watched the head football coach of the University of Alabama, Nick Saban, use the word "copycat" to describe the plays Clemson used to defeat Alabama in the title game. He said they used "copycat" plays, inferring that they used plays that Oklahoma had used to score against them! Exactly! So that is my message to young people: go find a great business and copy it. Doing so is easy with Google at your disposal to research anything and everything you need to know about a business.

Did you know that Walmart, one of the greatest businesses in the history of the world, came about this way? It is hard to believe, but Sam Walton says it himself. In his book, *Made in America*, he writes, "Walmart was built almost entirely off of other retailers' good ideas." He even goes on to say, "Most everything I've done I've copied from someone else." He explained that when he was working one of his first retail jobs, he would visit the store across the street and look at everything from their pricing to their displays. When he eventually built his first Walmart, he copied everything from that competitor.

I say, "There are no original thoughts," so go out there, and learn how to do it. As a side note, some people in my hometown call my place "Clay Mart." They are not giving me a compliment, but I am proud of my business either way. The copycat method has worked well for me.

8.  I have other business tips as well. Even if you end up working for someone else, they will help you to advance. **One of my biggest tips is to hustle.** As you know by now, energy and enthusiasm are part of my life, and they are imperative in business. "Run everywhere you go."

9.  **"Work while you eat"** is another tip. If I am having lunch, I am working. I believe you have to work *on* your business, not *in* your business. Sometimes my lunch hour is that time for me. We kick around all kinds of ideas during this time.

10. Finally, **have a team-like philosophy.** My team holds regular meetings and encourages all to speak up. Make your "Top Six" list per Earl Nightingale (we learned about this in Chapter 9). Whether you are running

your own company or working for somebody else, you can still operate as a "team," either by asking for help from your counterparts or by organizing strategy sessions for your employees to get together and discuss business ideas, suggestions for improving processes, and the like.

Do you know what President Harry S. Truman had on his desk? It was a sign that read, "The buck stops here." I tell my kids over and over again, it is called *responsibility*. You are responsible for everything that happens to you, so carpe diem. Take control of your finances today. Study hard, and formulate a plan. If you don't map out your financial future, you will go nowhere. Do it for your kids. Winners Travel to financial health.

# CHAPTER 15

# Winners Travel for Life

*"You only get out of it what you put into it!"*
— Clay Lowder

D O YOU REMEMBER COACH FAULKNER from
Chapter 1? He is the one who said, "Never a dull moment,
never a wasted second!" I will tell you another saying that he
taught me.

He would sometimes ask a current-events question like,
"Who is the prime minister of Great Britain?"

"Ummm," I would say.

"Five, four, three, two, one . . .BUZZ!" he would bellow.

Time was up! If I had not blurted out "Margaret Thatcher"
by "BUZZ," I was out of the game.

So now, I would like to pass this game along to you, putting *you* on the spot.

Here is the question: How has your life gone so far?

Five, four, three, two, one . . . BUZZ!

If you said, "Great, Clay, it has been great. I would not change a thing!" well then, congratulations! You can stop reading. You are among the 5 percent of people who "make the grade." Well done.

But if you hesitated, if you want more, if you believe you have messed up your life, I am here to help you start fixing it today. It is halftime, folks; it is not over! There is still time on the clock, but we have to start today.

As I've stressed over and over, plan to be a winner. Plan to travel. Plan to dream big. Plan to be somebody. How do you do that? I can help you.

I know it sounds scary, but you have to have a map. Imagine a ship leaving Myrtle Beach, South Carolina, and cruising to the Bahamas. Does the captain just "set sail" and let her go? No way! He has a map and a game plan. It is all charted out. In the case of bad weather causing the ship to be thrown off course, he simply returns to the map. The crew may panic, but the captain is decisive. He is in control and knows where he is going.

It is hard to believe that we do not plan our lives that way. Most people live *on* the earth but not *in* it. They work from eight to five every day, and repeat this pattern year after year. Sure, they think and occasionally dream, but they do not set out to change it. They do not act! They keep smoking, they keep drinking, they stay fat, they stay depressed, they stay lonely, and the list goes on.

Please do not be like those people. I feel called to put you on the spot. I promise I am not doing it to hurt you, but rather, to help you. Coach Faulkner wanted me to be a winner, and I want you to win too. It is time to embrace the idea that you were meant to live a full life—one that is healthy mentally, physically, and spiritually.

> **It is time to embrace the idea that you were meant to live a full life—one that is healthy mentally, physically, and spiritually.**

I hope that you will adopt a Winners Travel mentality. And I hope you have seen how traveling down the right path matters. First though, you have to visualize doing so.

When I ask the question of my teenage patients, "Where do you see yourself in ten years?" they giggle. They squirm. And only one in a hundred can even mutter a response. I ask them to write down their answer on an index card and bring it to me on their next visit. They often do. I hope and pray that in ten years, one of them sends me a text and picture of the life they created—the very life in which I lit a spark all those years ago.

Now, I am going to ask you to do the same thing. Please go get an index card, or turn to the blank pages at the back of this book, and write down the answer to the most important question:

## Where do you see yourself in ten years?

It is OK if you have never thought about your answer. It is not OK to dismiss it. It is never too late to start, and you can do so now. Here are some categories to help you get started:

(Fill in the blanks below.)

## Home

"I want to live in _____."

"I want a view of _____!"

"I want a man cave like this!" (Find a picture of one and paste it next to this statement!)

## Relationships

"I want my marriage to be like this: _____."

"I want my family to honor: _____."

"I want to have these types of friendships: _____."

## Vehicles

"I want a Chevy Corvette, 2015 edition, white with black trim." (That is my wife's dream!)

"I want a four-wheel-drive GMC truck."

"I want a boat."

(Be specific!)

## Mental Health

"I want to be fulfilled this way: _____."

"I will pursue happiness this way: _____."

## Physical Health

"I want to weigh _____."

"I want to look like this: (Cut out and paste a picture here!)"

## Spiritual Health

"I would like to have this special relationship: _____."

"I see myself serving God by serving others in this way: _____."

## Winners Travel (Grand Finale!)

"I would like to go on vacation here: _____."

"I would like to see this: _____."

"I would like to take my whole family here: _____."

I have always loved things of great beauty. When Kelliegh and I first married, we heard of a place called Atlantis. It's a towering resort in the Bahamas, and it is definitely a thing of beauty. Inside the hotel is a huge saltwater aquarium that's built to look like the lost underwater city of Atlantis. There's even a waterslide that travels through a shark tank! Kelliegh and I really couldn't afford it, but we set out to go anyway. Just like when we first discussed our dreams of owning a farm together and aligning our visions for our future, we were already living the Winners Travel mentality back then.

When we eventually made it to Atlantis, Kelliegh and I had a blast. We had long talks on the beach and asked each other about our dreams. The whole atmosphere at Atlantis inspired me. I had always been a big thinker, but the towers pushed me further. Through my readings, I learned to set goals. I just had never written them out. We spent a lot of time talking about our goals, but we'd never sat down and formed a game plan for our life together. As I've mentioned before, goals that are just thoughts are really just wishes. They materialize once you write them down and figure out the actions you will take to achieve them.

That week at Atlantis was slow and easy. One day on the beach, I asked Kelliegh to help me dream. I asked her to think. She did very well. We had tears in our eyes as we held hands and planned our future. There were hundreds of people around us on the beach, but it felt like just the two of us. We planned our family. We planned our house. We planned our faith. We planned our finances. It all just started gushing out of us. It was a "sun stand still" moment (when Joshua prays to God for the sun and moon to stand still, so that he and his army could continue fighting in daylight). A real "miracle moment." We decided then and there that we had to take vacations like this one for the rest of our lives. We had to have a time of reflection in which life slowed down and we could adjust our goals. We have done that. We have lived Winners Travel since that magical day.

There was one particular part of Atlantis that caught our eye. In between the two massive towers was a connecting bridge.

When we asked the staff what it was, they said, "Oh, you cannot go up there. That is Michael Jackson's suite. It sleeps twenty-five and rents for $25,000 per night!"

Kelliegh and I gawked.

We wrote down all our life's goals on that trip. When we got home, we cut out a picture of that bridge at Atlantis and took a pledge: "When we make it big time, we will rent that suite and take all of our family there with us!"

We hung that picture on the wall, and we have studied it for years and years since then. We have not yet reached our goal of taking everyone there, but we've still got time on the clock. It's in the game plan.

I know that's a fairly outlandish dream, and I am not asking you to do all that. I've told you this story to motivate you to dream as big as you want. I am asking you to consider where you would take your family.

I know that realistically not everyone can do this, which is why I have created the Winners Travel Foundation. It is a nonprofit organization to send people who are struggling financially on "dream trips." My heart is with caretakers, and I wanted to find a way to send them and their families to places they could never dream of actually going. Visit www.winnerstravel.org to see some of their stories. You can make a difference by giving. If we all pitch in, imagine how many people we can send!

\* \* \*

In fact, I just had an inspiration. I am going to send one of my caretakers that I see in my office to Atlantis. Maybe that is why my goal was so lofty!

Thank you, dear reader, for reading my book. I am so honored and humbled by your allowing me to share my life with you. I am deeply thankful to all of those who have led me and have never given up on me. I hope you will be inspired to change your life so that you, too, can find what you are seeking. And I hope that when you find it yourself, you will pass it on. I thank the Lord for the eternal gift of life and for allowing me to pass on what I have learned. I thank Him most of all for Winners Travel. I know He has big plans for me mentally, physically, and spiritually. I hope and pray that we can spread this concept to the world.

Winners Travel for life!

**Author's Note:** I was going to end my book here, but shortly after I finished the manuscript, something happened in my life that I just couldn't ignore. It was an event that gave me the opportunity to explore one more "Lowderism," and so I wrote an additional section, titled "You Only Have Ten Minutes."

# Final Thoughts: You Only Have Ten Minutes!

*"Everyone has a plan until they get punched in the mouth!"*
— Mike Tyson

I HEARD A NOISE. IT WAS actually two noises that sounded like pieces of aluminum clanging together. It was July 1, and I was in bed typing an email about the book launch of *Winners Travel.* I was grinning as I typed; I couldn't believe this was happening. Kelliegh and Liza were in the den watching *The Bachelorette,* and Clayton was in the basement with the TV cranked up as well. I sat up but dismissed the sounds. Maybe it was Clayton moving the ping-pong table.

Then it happened. The alarm started wailing. I jumped up and ran into the kitchen. Kelliegh beat me there.

"That's odd," she said calmly as she turned off the alarm.

"Did you set it?" I asked.

"Nope," she replied.

"I heard something outside. Did you?" I asked.

"Nope," she replied again.

I stepped outside anyway. I was looking for a burglar. When I saw and heard nothing, I turned to go back inside. Then I caught the faintest whiff of smoke. Have you ever heard people say, "Holy smoke"? I believe that's what it was. I asked Kelliegh to step out and see if she smelled it.

"Nope," she said for the third time and went back inside.

I walked toward the garage. When I peered in, I saw it. There was a cloud of deep black smoke billowing out the door.

"Fire!!" I screamed. "Get a water hose! Get out!" I yelled to my kids.

Liza and crew sprung into action. We got the water hose, and I went to the garage to put out whatever small thing I assumed was on fire, but I couldn't see through the smoke. After a minute, Clayton grabbed me and shook my shoulders.

"We've gotta go, Dad! It's gonna blow!"

I snapped out of it, and we ran far into the backyard.

I looked around. Clayton and Liza were there with me, but there was no Kelliegh.

"Oh my gosh! Kelliegh! Kelliegh!" I screamed over and over as I sprinted into the house.

When I entered the house, frantically looking for her, I ran right past her because of the panic, loud noises, and smoke. I ran to my room and library, and I kept screaming her name. I heard no response. I could hear the fire coming now, and it made a deep growl. I ran back toward the kitchen, and Kelliegh finally answered my call. I found her standing at the alarm, frantically pushing the fire button to call the fire department.

"Get OUT! Get out *now!*" I insisted. She hadn't seen the garage yet, so she didn't know the extent of the fire. She seemed to be in shock. I grabbed her bright-pink T-shirt and practically dragged her. The fire was louder now, and I could hear some explosions behind us. I decided we shouldn't risk the back door, so we exited through the front door. When we were almost out, she stopped.

"Wait, where's Britches?" She was looking for Little Britches, my trusty squirrel dog that a patient had given to me.

I looked her in the eye. "We've gotta go *now!*"

When we got to the yard, I started screaming for Clayton and Liza, worried they'd gone back into the house to look for us. Thankfully, they had stayed outside, and they met us in the front yard near the pond. By the time we got across the bridge, our house was in flames.

We all fell to our knees and watched in horror as the columns crashed, falling one by one. The noise was deafening. You could feel the heat across the hay pasture, and the flames could be seen from five miles away. It was utter devastation.

It burned down in ten minutes.

Think about that. Ten minutes. Our dream home and all of our worldly possessions were gone in only ten minutes.

The firemen of Lee County and Sumter County rushed in and did their best. By then, we had made it to the road, and family and friends began showing up. First, Dr. Eddie Meyers and his family came. Jake Meyers is Liza's boyfriend, and he ran up and bear hugged her. It was good to see them. About forty more people came out and just hugged us and stood there while we watched.

It was well into the night and the mosquitoes were fierce. Kelliegh and Liza had pajamas on and no shoes. Clayton had on shorts and a T-shirt. Kelliegh looked me up and down and said, "Seriously?"

I gasped. I realized I had run out of the house in my boxers and reading glasses. Yep, that's it. And what boxers they were!

They were about ten years old, and the whole back side had a rip in it. Kelliegh had given them to me as a gag gift. They were so worn that she had thrown them in the trash several times, but I had rescued them. They had become her least favorite of my boxers. To top it off, they were purple with green pickles all over accompanied by the phrase, "Tickle my pickle." We could only shake our heads. I had no wallet, cell phone, truck, or anything else, but I had my "Tickle my pickle" underwear.

After 1 a.m., I gathered the group together, and we all held hands. I told them that our identity was in Christ and not in the house. I told them that "home" was in our hearts. I said that it hurt badly and that we would struggle, but we were grateful. We were thankful. We were alive. I said, "We know that you all love us, and we can feel the love. That's what matters the most."

I then prayed, and something came over me. It was a feeling of grace and love and peace. It was a sense that God was going to use this as a positive. I prayed that I didn't understand it, but that if God was going to use this for something good, I would accept it. The Bible says in Romans 8:28, "And we know that all things work together for good to those who love God." I had trusted him with many things in the past. It was going to have to be *all* things now.

Everything I'd had before had disappeared in ten minutes.

The next few days were rough. We stayed with Tripp, Kelliegh's brother-in-law. The gifts were unreal. People literally gave us the shirts off their backs. The love we were shown from Sumter and the surrounding counties was second to none. I was so proud. I was happy that I had chosen to come back here and practice. Now, it was pretty hard to accept all the grace and love. I hadn't known it could be that tough. I cried and cried. People who I thought didn't even like me brought me stuff. A lot of people gave me new underwear. Boy, news travels fast!

I was most proud of my family. They stepped up and handled the ordeal with gratitude. Liza wrote a beautiful tribute on Facebook. She started with the story about how Kelliegh and I were high school sweethearts and had written out our "plantation home" dream together. You'll remember from an earlier chapter that for our anniversary one year, I surprised Kelliegh with a trip across South Carolina to take pictures of old plantation homes. We took pictures of what we wanted and made a dream scrapbook. It took well over a decade to plot and plan and build our house. Then it was gone into thin air.

Mike Tyson said, "Everyone has a plan until they get punched in the mouth!" We got sucker punched. How would we handle it?

Well, we started with a Facebook Live video taken at the house. It went viral. You can watch it on my website. In it, I praised God for His protection and grace. What we had happen was tragic, but it wasn't a tragedy. We'd only lost Britches.

Then I asked my kids to say a few words. They took over, and they stole the show. I cried as I watched my life's work in my kids come to fruition. They had grown up with wealth, and I had tried all I could do not to spoil them. They shocked me with the "attitude of gratitude" we'd taught them. They told of their identity in Christ and not of material things. They were so grateful to God and the people of Sumter and Lee. Kelliegh and I have always made raising our kids our number one goal. We built that house in the country mainly because we thought farm living would teach them the right way. It worked. My home had done its job. God showed me right then and there that my kids would be all right no matter what. What a gift that was to me.

I told the kids on the way out to the house that I hoped and prayed that this would be the worst thing that ever happened to them. If so, life would be fine. I meant it.

So, my recommendation to you is to find that gratitude in your heart. It's in there. Sometimes the battles and calluses of life won't let it out. Even if you have to fake it at first, just do it. Make a list and thank God and your family for all they have done. Thank Him for the freedom to do what you want in the greatest country in the history of the world!

Here's the Facebook post that I wrote that week:

# FIVE LESSONS LEARNED FROM THE FIRE
# THAT BURNED MY HOUSE DOWN

July 1, 2019
By Clay Lowder

1. I'm so thankful.

I'm thankful to be alive. I'm grateful my family got out in the nick of time. When I went outside to check for a burglar, I smelled the "faintest whisper of smoke." I believe God blew it on me. I believe He led us out. Two hours later, I don't think we'd make it out. I wouldn't have come out without all my family.

I'm thankful to this community. I'm thankful to the Lee and Sumter Fire Departments. They did their best. I'm thankful to all the folks who've given beyond belief. I'm thankful to my partners who've reached out. I'm thankful to my patients. I'm thankful to my staff, who handed me money, money they don't even have. I'm grateful to all the people on social media who sent prayers and love. I'm amazed. I have so many friends. People I thought that didn't even like me reached out! They prayed for me. It's truly humbling.

I'm so thankful.

2. I have a lot of families.

> I have a Sumter, Lee, and Clarendon family. I have a church family. I have a Colonial family. I have a Wilson Hall family. I have a Clemson family. They have reached out nonstop. I'm so glad I came home. I'm so proud to be from here. I love the South. I love being a Baron and a Tiger.
>
> Most importantly, I love being a Lowder. I'm thankful to my parents, who raised me in the country. I knew the impact it had on me. I built this home for that reason. Kelliegh and I dreamed this up in high school. We knew we wanted to raise our family here. It worked. They have country values. They have a deep appreciation for life. One of the best things I've seen is the way my kids handled this. I've been amazed by them. Material things are not important to them. They have Christ in them. They will be OK. This may be my biggest gift in all this. It's a God wink that my kids will be OK. This home did its job.
>
> I have a lot of families.

3. Grace is hard to accept.

> The gifts are extreme. People have literally given me the shirt off their back. I can hardly take it. Thank you all.

I knew grace in my head. I knew it intellectually. But now I know it in my heart. Wow. It's an experience.

I tell people all the time about grace. All you have to do is accept it. But I didnt know how difficult that was. I've learned it's hard for me. I will handle people differently after this. I will accept it.

Grace is hard to accept.

4. I'm not as tough as I thought.

I'm weak. I'm vulnerable. I try not to let people see that side of me. Maybe that's why I act so strong. This buckled me. I have deep fears. But maybe that vulnerability will make me stronger. My faith is based on that. I guess if I could do it all, I wouldn't need a savior. I'm going to let it go.

I'm not as tough as I thought.

5. You only have 10 minutes.

Here's the biggest lesson. Everything I had built and dreamed and accomplished by material standards burned in 10 minutes. We barely got out. In fact, I ran out in my worn-out boxers and reading glasses (Side note: wear good underwear to bed. My whole backside was ripped.)

My message and my book is *Winners Travel*. It's a doctor's guide to mental, spiritual, and physical health. I just got the ending. It's something like this:

Don't wait for the obituary to tell someone what they mean to you!!

Do it now. Do it today. We call it The Compliment Game. I challenge you to ask your family at dinner to play it. Go around the table, and tell each person the best thing about them and what they mean to you. It will change your life. I just got to play it with all my families at once, and it feels amazing.

Nothing else matters. Nothing is more important than your relationships. I promise your "stuff" doesn't matter.

If you need to call or text someone a compliment, Do It Now!!!

You only have 10 minutes.

I love you all!

— Clay

So there you have it. I got punched in the mouth. Most of you have as well. But I won't allow that to derail my family or me. I figure, if I'm the Winners Travel guy, then I need to be able to live it now. Remember, we are never too old to set new goals, and that's what the Lowders are doing. It won't be perfect or easy. In fact, it hurts deeply, but I feel that with God's help, I will be able to rebuild my life bigger and better than ever. Maybe that is the key to a Winners Travel life: that you are always looking out the windshield. Forget about the rearview mirror, and move on.

Thank you for being a Winner. My prayer is that some way, somehow, this book will move you to change your life and change it *now*. Remember, you only have ten minutes!

WINNERS TRAVEL FOR LIFE!

— Clay

# Winners Travel Mini Workbook

Now that you've finished reading *Winners Travel*, I hope you are already thinking about the ways you can improve your mental, physical, and spiritual self.

Use the following pages to write down your goals, thoughts, and answers to some of the questions that I asked throughout the book.

## WHERE DO YOU SEE YOURSELF IN TEN YEARS?

Answer any or all of these questions: "What does your house look like?" "What does your spouse look like?" "Where do you see yourself working?" Get specific too. "How much money do you make?" "What kind of dog do you have?" "What's your dream vacation?" "How many kids do you want?" "What do they look like?" "What names do you like?"

## WHO IS CURRENTLY IN YOUR TOP FIVE?

## WHO DO YOU WANT TO ADD TO YOUR TOP FIVE AND WHY THAT PERSON?

# WHAT GOOD HABITS DO YOU PRACTICE?

# WHAT BAD HABITS WOULD YOU LIKE TO KICK? HOW WILL YOU COMMIT TO GETTING RID OF THOSE HABITS?

Play "the compliment game" below. Write down a few names of friends, family, anybody, and then write down a compliment next to their name. Now, call them and read the compliment to them!!

Name: _____

Compliment: _____

Name: _____

Compliment: _____

Name: _____

Compliment: _____

Name: _____

Compliment: _____

Name: _____

Compliment: _____

# DO YOU HAVE A GAME PLAN FOR LIFE—YOUR HEALTH? YOUR CAREER? YOUR SPIRITUAL JOURNEY? WRITE IT DOWN!

# NOW, IF YOU ONLY HAD 10 MINUTES ... WHAT WOULD YOU DO? WHO WOULD YOU CALL,

Made in the USA
Columbia, SC
15 June 2023